Social History of Medicine

Published by the Society of the Social History of Medicine

Volume 18 Number 1: April 2005

Contents

Please visit the journal's website at http://www.shm.oupjournals.org

Published by Oxford University Press

Social History of Medicine Vol. 18 No. 1
doi:10.1093/sochis/hki025

Editorial Note

The editors would like to express their thanks and convey their scholarly appreciation to their predecessor. Roger Davidson maintained a high standard of editorial scrutiny and efficiency. His unremitting patience, clarity of style and promptness of action did much to ease the pressures associated with editorial duties.

The new editorial team regrets that from April 2005 Louise Curth will no longer be able to act as reviews editor. This is due to other professional commitments. We thank her for her efforts and commitment, and wish her well for her future career.

The editors would like to invite applications for the position of reviews editor, to be taken up from April 2005 or soon after. Candidates should send a *curriculum vitae*, publication list, and a sample of their written work to the Assistant Editor.

scholars.[2] Until now, however, it has never been tested through a study of medical practice. One excellent test case is for Britain, *circa* 1600–1740. A study of this period is critical in determining the role of 'sex' in British medical practice for two reasons. First, it is believed to be a pivotal period in Britain for the development of the medical profession and the emergence of male-centred care of women.[3] Secondly, it is the earliest period for which evidence of actual medical practice exists in reasonable abundance.

In order to evaluate the validity of the one-sex model for this period, one central question for the historian is to determine whether or not male and female patients were prescribed identical treatments for the same illnesses. For the purpose of this article, three common diseases have been selected for special consideration: venereal disease, smallpox, and malaria. It is important to recognize that early modern and present-day nosologies do not completely overlap.[4] Thus, the diagnostic categories referred to in this article correspond, as closely as possible, to those employed in the primary sources. Although the evidence often does not indicate exactly *how* practitioners differentiated between specific diagnoses

[2] Supporters include: L. Schiebinger, 'Skeletons in the Closet: The First Illustrations of the Female Skeleton in Eighteenth-Century Anatomy', in Gallagher and Laqueur (eds), *The Making of the Modern Body*, 42–82; idem, *The Mind has No Sex?: Women in the Origins of Modern Science* (Cambridge, MA, and London, 1989); idem, 'Skelettestreit', *Isis*, 94 (2003), 307–13; S. Greenblatt, 'Fiction and Friction', in *Shakespearean Negotiations: The Circulation of Social Energy in Renaissance England* (Oxford, 1988), 66–93, esp. pp. 76–86; R. Porter, 'History of the Body', in P. Burke (ed.), *New Perspectives on Historical Writing* (University Park, Pennsylvania, 1991), 206–32, pp. 220–1; idem, 'History of the Body Reconsidered', in P. Burke (ed.), *New Perspectives on Historical Writing*, 2nd edn (University Park, Pennsylvania, 2001), 233–60, pp. 249–50; B. Duden, *The Woman Beneath the Skin: A Doctor's Patients in Eighteenth-Century Germany*, trans. T. Dunlap (Cambridge, MA, and London, 1991), pp. 1, 20–41, 112–19, 183–4; A. Fletcher, *Gender, Sex and Subordination in England 1500–1800* (New Haven, 1995), pp. 30–59; R. McGrath, *Seeing her Sex: Medical Archives and the Female Body* (Manchester and New York, 2002).

[3] T. Gelfand, 'The History of the Medical Profession', in W. F. Bynum and R. Porter (eds), *Companion Encyclopedia of the History of Medicine*, 2 vols, vol. II (London and New York, 1993), 1119–50; H. J. Cook, 'Good Advice and Little Medicine: The Professional Authority of Early Modern English Physicians', *Journal of British Studies*, 33 (1994), 1–31; R. O'Day, 'The Organization of Professional Medicine in England', in *The Professions in Early Modern England, 1450–1800: Servants of the Commonweal*, Themes in British Social History (Harlow and New York, 2000), 185–203; H. Smith, 'Gynaecology and Ideology in Seventeenth-Century England', in B. A. Carroll (ed.), *Liberating Women's History: Theoretical and Critical Essays* (Urbana, Chicago, and London, 1976), 97–114; A. Eccles, *Obstetrics and Gynaecology in Tudor and Stuart England* (London, 1982); D. Porter and R. Porter, 'Doctors and Women', in idem, *Patient's Progress: Doctors and Doctoring in Eighteenth-Century England* (Cambridge, 1989), 173–85; E. Shorter, *A History of Women's Bodies: A Social History of Women's Encounter with Health, Ill-Health, and Medicine* (New York, 1982; repr. edn. New Brunswick, NJ, 1991); A. Wilson, *The Making of Man-Midwifery: Childbirth in England, 1660–1770* (London and Cambridge, MA, 1995).

[4] See W. F. Bynum, 'Nosology', in Bynum and Porter (eds), *Companion Encyclopedia*, vol. I, 335–56; A. Wear, *Knowledge and Practice in English Medicine, 1550–1680* (Cambridge and New York, 2000), pp. 13–14, 104–8. For a discussion of early modern nosologies of venereal disease, smallpox, and malaria, see A. M. Brandt, 'Sexually Transmitted Diseases', in Bynum and Porter (eds), *Companion Encyclopedia*, vol. I, 562–84, esp. p. 567; J. Arrizabalaga, J. Henderson, and R. French, *The Great Pox: The French Disease in Renaissance Europe* (New Haven and London, 1997), pp. 1–19; K. P. Siena, *Venereal Disease, Hospitals and the Urban Poor: London's 'Foul Wards', 1600–1800*, Rochester Studies in Medical History (Rochester, 2004), pp. 15–22, 173, 264–5; M. J. Dobson, *Contours of Death and Disease in Early Modern England*, Cambridge Studies in Population, Economy and Society in Past Time, XXIX (Cambridge and New York, 1997), esp. pp. 233–41, 310, 317, 321, 472, 474–5.

(such as gonorrhoea and gynaecological ailments in female patients), it is clear that they did so from their use of separate diagnostic categories. Although venereal disease affected different sexual organs in female and male patients, the general aetiology, diagnostics, and prognostics—like those of malaria and smallpox—were regarded as essentially the same in both sexes.[5] One might suppose these illnesses to have been neutral in their manifestation in men and women, adults and children, thus offering the historian of medicine a unique series of tests by which to determine the prevalence of a 'sexed' model of treatment within seventeenth- and early eighteenth-century British medicine. This investigation will demonstrate that, despite sharing an inheritance of the Galenic theory of the body which produced a number of similarities, 'sex' was a category, based on a medical recognition of biological, physiological differences, that clearly influenced diagnosis and treatment. Although there were a number of similarities in diagnosing, treating, and dosing male and female patients, practitioners were aware that women possessed unique physiological functions—including vaginal discharge, menstruation, pregnancy, and lactation—all of which provided additional reasons to monitor, and alter, treatment. In fact, the different humoural constitutions of men and women meant that the treatment model was much more complex than the theory of a one-sex model suggests.[6]

I

Some scholars now acknowledge that the one-sex model fails to satisfy the complexities of seventeenth-century medicine.[7] In particular, the straightforward, linear progression from a one-sex model to a two-sex model has recently been

[5] For instance, see Wellcome Library for the History and Understanding of Medicine MS (hereafter Wellcome) 7501 (Anonymous practitioner's casebook, Scotland, 1726–41), fol. 4; The Royal College of Physicians of London MS (hereafter RCP) 5 (Samuel England, 'Chirgical Observations', 1730–3), n.p. ('of the Herpes' and 'observations of a Gonorrhoea, Inflammation of the Penis &c.'); F. N. L. Poynter and W. J. Bishop (eds), *A Seventeenth-Century Doctor and His Patients: John Symcotts, 1592? – 1662*, Publications of the Bedfordshire Historical Record Society, XXXI (Streatley, Bedfordshire, 1951), p. 19; Thomas Willis, *The London Practice of Physick, being the Practical Part of Physick Contain'd in the Works of the Famous Dr Willis* ... (London, 1692; repr. edn, Boston, 1973), pp. 534–55, 622–33; John Astruc, *A Treatise of the Venereal Disease, in Six Books* ..., trans. William Barrowby, 2 vols, vol. I (London, 1737; repr. edn, New York and London, 1985), pp. 247–73, 303–13, 357–68, 385–8, 390–4, 399–413; idem, *A Treatise of the Venereal Disease*, vol. II, pp. 1–94.

[6] Through her examination of political and legal sources, Ulinka Rublack reached a similar conclusion regarding the social, physical, and emotional experiences related to gestation and parturition in early modern Germany. U. Rublack, 'Pregnancy, Childbirth and the Female Body in Early Modern Germany', *Past and Present*, 150 (1996), 84–110, p. 86.

[7] For instance, see J. Sawday, *The Body Emblazoned: Dissection and the Human Body in Renaissance Culture* (London and New York, 1995), pp. 184–8, 192, 194, 213–29, see esp. pp. 213–15, 221; J. Adelman, 'Making Defect Perfection: Shakespeare and the One-Sex Model', in V. Comensoli and A. Russell (eds), *Enacting Gender on the Renaissance Stage* (Urbana and Chicago, 1999), 23–52; G. Pomata, 'Menstruating Men: Similarity and Difference of the Sexes in Early Modern Medicine', in V. Finucci and K. Brownlee (eds), *Generation and Degeneration: Tropes of Reproduction in Literature and History from Antiquity through Early Modern Europe* (Durham, NC and London, 2001), 109–52, esp. pp. 111–13, 152; K. Harvey, 'The Substance of Sexual Difference: Change and Persistence in Representations of the Body in Eighteenth-Century England', *Gender and History*, 14 (2002), 202–23;

subjected to close scrutiny. In his work on the Renaissance culture of human dissection, Jonathan Sawday has argued that:

> [sixteenth- and seventeenth-century] biological theory is far more complex than the 'one-sex' model tends to allow, since that model tends to ignore the quasi-autonomous nature of the uterus—that Medusa's head—in early-modern physiological discourse. Equally, the 'one-sex' model tends to ignore the fluid metaphoric language with which men and women in early-modern culture described their own bodies.[8]

In her examination of Shakespearean and medical texts, Janet Adelman suggested that there was 'a complex conversation about anatomical sexual difference—a conversation that we are not likely to hear if we know in advance that there is only one way to think anatomically about sexual difference in the Renaissance'.[9] Gianna Pomata has argued that extant stories of menstruating men undermine the theory that the male body was regarded as the standard structural paradigm for the human body in early modern European medicine until, at least, the late 1700s.[10] Helen King has questioned the validity of Laqueur's evolutionary two-sex model by demonstrating its existence within the Hippocratic gynaecology of classical Greece.[11]

Despite such challenges, however, there remains a reluctance to dismiss entirely the existence of the one-sex model. For instance, Robert Martensen questioned the 'hegemony of the one-sex model in pre-Enlightenment Western thought' by arguing that anatomical drawings represented 'male and female as both similar and different, as both one-sex and two-sex'. Nevertheless, he maintained that '[t]he main theoretical cleavage point ... was the difference between male and female economies of fluid. ... [T]he womb and its fluids were [assumed to be] much more important in women than the penis and its fluids in men'.[12] And although Winfried Schleiner postulated that the one-sex model was challenged by at least two seventeenth-century continental physicians, he nonetheless ascribed to the notion that the normative model for this period was one-sexed.[13] Lisa W. Smith has also downplayed the awareness of anatomical and physiological differences between the bodies of men and women by arguing that, prior to diagnosis, male and female patients described their experiences of

M. Stolberg, 'A Woman Down to Her Bones: The Anatomy of Sexual Difference in the Sixteenth and Early Seventeenth Centuries', *Isis*, 94 (2003), 274–99.

[8] Sawday, *The Body Emblazoned*, p. 214.

[9] Adelman, 'Making Defect Perfection', p. 25 (see also pp. 39–42).

[10] Pomata, 'Menstruating Men', pp. 112–13, 152.

[11] H. King, *Hippocrates' Woman: Reading the Female Body in Ancient Greece* (London and New York, 1998), pp. 7–8, 11. See also Adelman, 'Making Defect Perfection', esp. pp. 25–6, 39–42; Pomata, 'Menstruating Men', esp. pp. 111–13, 138, 151–2; R. Flemming, *Medicine and the Making of Roman Women: Gender, Nature, and Authority from Celsus to Galen* (Oxford and New York, 2000), pp. 12–16, 23, 119–21, 357–8, 371–2.

[12] R. Martensen, 'The Transformation of Eve: Women's Bodies, Medicine, and Culture in Early Modern England', in R. Porter and M. Teich (eds), *Sexual Knowledge, Sexual Science: The History of Attitudes to Sexuality* (Cambridge and New York, 1994), 107–33, p. 113 (see also pp. 107–17, 128–9). Karen Harvey has also supported this view. See Harvey, 'The Substance of Sexual Difference', esp. pp. 204–5, 211, 213–14, 218–19.

[13] W. Schleiner, 'Early Modern Controversies about the One-Sex Model', *Renaissance Quarterly*, 53 (2000), 180–91.

pain and illness in similar ways.[14] Smith asserts that '[b]alance was the key to both men's and women's medical treatment, not the possession of different sexual organs'.[15]

Previous scholarship has tended to focus on the printed medical literature, particularly on anatomical writings and drawings of genitalia and reproductive organs which appear to have highlighted the similarities, rather than differences, between men and women.[16] As a consequence, there has been a tendency to dismiss the important role that sex-specific physiological functions played in the different constitutions of the male body and the female body. A notable exception to this trend is Gail Kern Paster, who has argued that medical theories regarding menstrual bleeding and physiological differences in 'innate heat' indicate the existence of a two-sex body model in seventeenth-century England.[17] Paster draws primarily upon vernacular medical treatises and plays, in order to establish the social and cultural importance of the humoural body, rather than manuscript sources (such as casebooks) pertaining to medical practice.

While an emphasis on medical theory is valuable, this preoccupation has been largely at the expense of determining what happened in actual practice. As Andrew Wear has recently demonstrated, it is important to remember that medical theory never existed in isolation from medical practice, or *vice versa*.[18] As such, there remains a need to determine how practitioners' theories regarding their patients' bodies were applied in practice. This article will therefore seek to redress this imbalance by utilizing four main categories of evidence: practitioner casebooks; patient–practitioner correspondence; practitioner consultation letters; and medical tracts. Only a small number of these primary sources have been published; the bulk of evidence is drawn from the manuscript collections at the British Library, the Royal College of Physicians of London, and the Wellcome Library for the History and Understanding of Medicine.

II

At first glance, the medical treatment provided to male and female patients who presented the same symptoms appear to have been very similar or, at times, even identical. In the case of venereal disease, which covered a wide variety of sexually-transmitted ailments that are now viewed as separate, patients of both sexes were generally prescribed the same types of treatments. Until the mid-eighteenth century, gonorrhoea and syphilis were considered to be different

[14] L. W. Smith, 'Women's Health Care in England and France (1650–1775)' (unpublished Ph.D. thesis, University of Essex, 2001), pp. 10–12, 33–9, 45–6, 90–131, 269.

[15] Ibid., p. 45.

[16] For instance, Laqueur, *Making Sex*, esp. pp. 4–5, 25–62; Fletcher, 'Functional Anatomies', in Fletcher, *Gender, Sex and Subordination*, 30–43; McGrath, *Seeing her Sex*.

[17] See G. Kern Paster, *The Body Embarrassed: Drama and the Disciplines of Shame in Early Modern England* (Ithaca, 1993), esp. pp. 8, 10, 16–17, 79–83, 166–7; idem, 'The Unbearable Coldness of Female Being: Women's Imperfection and the Humoral Economy', *English Literary Renaissance*, 28 (1998), 416–40.

[18] Wear, *Knowledge and Practice*.

progressions in the manifestation of the same underlying disease.[19] While guaiacum and mercury represented the principal treatments, men and women alike were also given prescriptions containing china-root, sarsaparilla, and sassafras-wood.[20] They were administered 'fluxing' treatments—such as mercurial salivations—intended to flush the venereal 'poison' out of the body and anointed with ointments aimed at healing ulcers.[21] In the printed case histories from his Jamaican medical practice of 1687–8, Hans Sloane (1660–1753) claimed that by prescribing the same purges, vomits, and emulsions for all gonorrhoeal patients he had 'never failed the Cure of any, either Man or Woman'.[22]

Smallpox was another highly infectious disease for which practitioners commonly diagnosed and treated male and female patients. Prior to widespread inoculation, smallpox was treated with internal 'physick' (often containing cloves, cinnamon, or hyssop) and external remedies such as ointments, plasters, blistering, and bloodletting. These methods could be administered for either the prevention or the treatment of the disease, functioning to promote healing, ease discomfort, and reduce scarification.[23] As with venereal patients, adult male and female smallpox patients were often administered similar treatments. In his account entries for 1703, a West Yorkshire apothecary recorded identical prescriptions, including dosages, for smallpox in a seven-year-old girl and an eight-year-old boy.[24] In the case of these pre-pubescent patients, at least, sex alone does not appear to have affected the treatment.

During the 1600s and 1700s, malaria—identified at that time as intermittent fevers or agues—was endemic within large portions of the British empire and

[19] Brandt, 'Sexually Transmitted Diseases', esp. p. 567; Siena, *Venereal Disease*, p. 15. For more on the nosology of venereal disease and the problems of retrospective diagnosis (especially in regard to syphilis), see Arrizabalaga, Henderson, and French, *The Great Pox*, pp. 1–19; Siena, *Venereal Disease*, pp. 15–22, 173, 264–5.

[20] Astruc, *A Treatise of the Venereal Disease*, vol. I, esp. pp. i, ii, ix, 170–92, 227–46; Wellcome 6919 (Nicholas Gaynsford's case notes, 1712–13), fol. 31v; Wellcome 3631 (Alexander Morgan's casebook, 1714–47), p. 28. See Arrizabalaga, Henderson, and French, *The Great Pox*, pp. 32, 82–4, 100–4, 137, 140, 187–90, 203, 231–2, 240–1, 267, 280; Siena, *Venereal Disease*, pp. 45, 64, 83–4.

[21] Wellcome 6888 (Clinical lectures of John Rutherford, recorded by an unknown student at Edinburgh Royal Infirmary, 1748/9), fol. 167r; British Library (hereafter BL) Sloane MS (hereafter Sl.) 1055 (Prescriptions and cases of a physician in London, 1638–43, after in Lancaster and Chester, 1651–62, fols. 31–113), fols. 51v – 2r, 72, 74r.

[22] Hans Sloane, *A Voyage to the Islands Madera, Barbados, Nieves, S. Christophers and Jamaica, with the Natural History of the Herbs and Trees, Four-footed Beasts, Fishes, Birds, Insects, Reptiles, &c. of the Last of those Islands* ..., 2 vols, vol. I (London, 1707), p. cxxviii. All dates are given as they appear in the sources.

[23] For instance, see John Hall, *Select Observations on English Bodies of Eminent Persons in Desperate Diseases* ..., trans. James Cook (London, 1679), pp. 69–70 (observation LXXVIII), 154–5 (observation LXIV); Wellcome 5005 (Observations on particular Cases of Patients and how treated by Dr [Richard] Wilkes, from 1731 to 1742. Collected from scattered Remains of the Dr's own Hand writing [by] Thomas Unett. And continued by Richard Wilkes Unett from MSS. of Dr Wilkes), pp. 31–2, 37–45, 66–71, 86–7; Wellcome 7500 (Apothecary's Cash-Book, West Yorkshire, 1703–10), fols. 140r – 1r; Wellcome 7501, fols. 19r – 22r; BL Sl. 1589 (Sir Edmund King's casebook, 1676–96), fols. 128v – 32v, 241r.

[24] Wellcome 7500, fol. 140r.

in regions of southern England.[25] Practitioners treated patients with prescriptions containing either mithridate or cinchona, or applied poultices directly to the skin.[26] Internal remedies containing cinchona could be administered in the form of powders, pills, or electuaries.[27] Male and female patients alike were administered these remedies, in addition to blisters, purges, enemas, and bloodletting.[28] As with the prescriptions for smallpox, the prescribed dosages for malarial remedies did not adhere to a clear delineation based upon the patient's sex. Rather, the amounts reflected the patient's entire constitution, incorporating variations in sex, age, body size, and symptoms. In his late seventeenth-century medical commonplace book, the Cambridge-trained physician, Phineas Fowke (1638–1710), recorded that, according to one Dr Dickinson, 'intermitting Fevers' were best treated by administering at least half an ounce of cinchona between fits 'to a man, or woman, or to a youth or mayd [who was] allmost at full state [of health following a fit]'.[29] Practitioners often began with the same treatment methods and minimum standard dosages, but adjusted these amounts and methods according to the age of the patient, the strength of the patient's constitution, and the responsiveness of the patient's symptoms.[30]

It appears, then, that practitioners customarily administered the same types of remedies to male and female patients who exhibited identical symptoms of illness. A closer examination of the evidence, however, reveals that the

[25] For instance, see Wellcome 2433 (Phineas Fowke, Medical common-place book, circa 1690), p. 84; BL SL. 275, fols. 7r, 10r, 11v, 27v, 31v, 47v, 48r, 73v, 83r; BL SL. 78, fols. 158v, 173r; BL SL. 80, fols. 23r, 34, 35, 42r; Sloane, *A Voyage*, pp. cxxxiv–vi. For occurrences in the Scottish context, see Wellcome 7501, fols. 4r, 5, 23, 24; Wellcome 6888, fols. 15v, 16r, 18r. For more on malaria in early modern England, see Dobson, *Contours of Death and Disease.*

[26] Wellcome 5005, p. 66; Wellcome 7500, fols. 1r – 3v, 34v – 5v; BL Sl. 1589, fol. 291v; J. E. Ward and J. Yell (eds), *The Medical Casebook of William Brownrigg, MD, FRS (1712–1800) of the Town of Whitehaven in Cumberland*, Medical History Supplement, XIII (London, 1993), pp. 57, 97–9.

[27] Wellcome 2433, p. 69; BL Sl. 1589, fol. 291v; Wellcome 7500, fol. 3r; Wellcome 5005, p. 68; RCP 513 (Collection of medical and culinary recipes, *circa* 1667–71 and prescriptions, 1722), p. 35; RCP 625 (Alexander Stuart and William Wasey, Westminster Infirmary casebook, 1723–4), 6 August 1723, 17 and 18 September 1723, 1 and 2 October 1723, 10 and 17 December 1723.

[28] For instance, see Wellcome 5006 (Richard Wilkes, Diary and Observations from 1 January 1739 to 7 July 1754. Copied from the original by Richard Wilkes Unett), p. 60; BL Sl. 80 (John Pratt, Register of cases and prescriptions, Cambridge, 1646–61), fols. 23r, 34, 35, 42r; BL Sl. 1408 (Prescriptions chiefly by Dr Gosling, Cambridge, 1626–8), fols. 2, 21, 22r – 4r, 26, 30r – 1r, 35, 37r, 41r – 3v.

[29] Wellcome 2433, p. 69. This 'Dr Dickinson' was probably the royal physician and alchemist Edmund Dickinson, MD (1624–1707), who then held positions as one of the physicians in ordinary to King Charles II and physician to the household. See *The Dictionary of National Biography* (hereafter *DNB*), s.v. 'Dickinson or Dickenson, Edmund, MD'; W. Munk, 'Edmund Dickinson, MD', in *The Roll of the Royal College of Physicians of London: Comprising Biographical Sketches of All Eminent Physicians*, 2nd edn, 5 vols (London, 1878), I (1518–1700), 394–6.

[30] Wellcome 2433, pp. 69–71; RCP 206/4 (George Colebrook [d. 1716], Extracts from letters on medical cases, *circa* 1690), pp. 98–9 ([George Colebrook] to Dr Carver, n.d.), 116 ([Dr Wrench], n.d.), 117 ([Dr Wrench], n.d.), 136 ([Dr Wrench], n.d.); Wellcome 6919, fol. 26r; Sloane, *A Voyage*, pp. cxv, cxxiii; Wellcome 7501, fol. 55v; Willis, *The London Practice*, pp. 630–3; John Page, *Receipts for Preparing and Compounding the Principal Medicines Made Use of By the Late Mr Ward* ... (London, 1763), pp. 7, 8, 13, 32. The 'late Mr Ward' was the irregular practitioner, Joshua Ward (1685–1761), who was famous for his polychrest nostrums. See *DNB*, s.v. 'Ward, Joshua'.

physiological differences between men and women did, in fact, significantly influence medical treatment. First, practitioners frequently noted the importance of sexual difference in their medical casebooks, correspondence, and treatises. Dr Barker, a Shrewsbury physician practising around 1600, noted that, in addition to age and temperament, 'sex' was among the considerations in prescribing treatments for his patients.[31] More than 70 years later, this sentiment was echoed in the work of physician, Gideon Harvey (1640? – 1700?), who criticized mountebanks for a lack of regard concerning their patients' 'Constitution, Age, [and] Sex'.[32] This same view is also evident amongst the mid-eighteenth-century clinical lectures of John Rutherford (1695–1779), Professor of Medicine at the University of Edinburgh, 1726–65. According to the lecture notes of an unidentified student at the Edinburgh Royal Infirmary, Rutherford asserted that a dogmatic (or rational) physician, due to reason and practice, recognized 'that the same Disease in different Persons of different Constitutions will require a different Method of Cure'.[33] On the other hand, Rutherford held that an empiric (i.e. a medical practitioner with no formal training, widely considered to be inferior by university-educated physicians) was one who 'practise[d] by rote [i.e. routine] and d[id] not direct his Remedy to the Disease but to the Name of the Disease ... and so without considering the Constitution of the Patient'.[34] From the perspective of university-educated, 'learned' physicians, such as Barker, Harvey, and Rutherford, age, sex, and constitution were viewed as intertwined components of patient medical care throughout the seventeenth and early eighteenth centuries.

Practitioners believed that disease manifested itself differently in the female body than in the male body. They were, therefore, careful to distinguish between seemingly similar symptoms in men and women. Practitioners emphasized the importance of cautious observation and diagnosis of their female patients, in part, because disease symptoms were believed to be more easily masked by the female body than the male body.[35] For instance, while abnormal vaginal discharge could be considered to be symptomatic of venereal disease in women, practitioners also recognized that it could signify a female-specific ailment such as *fluor albus* (often referred to as 'the whites'), which was a common gynaecological ailment typified by vaginal discharge and back pain.[36]

[31] BL Sl. 79 (Barker, MD of Shrewsbury, Medical observations and memoranda, *circa* 1600, fols. 112–56), fols. 153r – 4r.

[32] Gideon Harvey, *The Family-Physician and the House-Apothecary* ... ([London?], [1676]), 'The Introduction, Containing the Use of this Treatise', n.p. [p. 4]. The italics found within quotations are those of the original author, unless otherwise noted.

[33] Wellcome 6888, fol. 1v. All palaeographical abbreviations have been silently expanded.

[34] Ibid., fol. 2r.

[35] Similarly, Cathy McClive has argued that pregnancy is one example of how the female body was capable of masking medical 'truths' in ways that were unavailable to the male body. See C. McClive, 'The Hidden Truths of the Belly: The Uncertainties of Pregnancy in Early Modern Europe', *Social History of Medicine*, 15 (2002), 209–27.

[36] See Robert James, *A Medicinal Dictionary* ..., 3 vols, vol. II (London, 1745), s.v. 'Fluor Albus'; J. A. Simpson and E. S. C. Weiner (eds), *The Oxford English Dictionary* (hereafter *OED*), 2nd edn, 20 vols, vol. V (Oxford, 1989), s.v. 'fluor albus'; *OED*, vol. VIII, s.v. 'leucorrhoea'; John Astruc, *A Treatise on all the Diseases Incident to Women* ..., trans. J. R—n (London, 1743; repr. edn, New York and London, 1985), p. 136.

Practitioners emphasized that it was necessary to inquire about the precise nature of the patient's symptoms in order to differentiate between the two conditions: if the white discharge ceased during menstruation, it was likely *fluor albus*; if not, it was probably gonorrhoea.[37] On the other hand, gonorrhoeal discharge in male patients was rarely, if ever, confused with seminal emissions. In his Oxford casebook, Thomas Willis (1621–75) had dismissed the possibility that men could experience abnormal seminal discharges (other than those of a venereal nature) akin to 'the whites' because 'it would be necessary for them to be brought to an extreme emaciation and consumption of the body, just as happens to those who have intercourse immoderately.'[38] Smallpox was also regarded as having different manifestations in different bodies. In 1681/2, Thomas Sydenham (1624–89) noted that the virulence of smallpox was dependent on the patient's age and sex, and concluded that 'every one knows, that a young man in the flower of his Age is much more in danger than a Woman or Boy'.[39] Although it was held that women and children—due to their moist natures—were more susceptible to the disease than men, they were also seen as more capable of withstanding its effects, in part due to the softness of their skin.[40] In his letter responding to a patient's queries, Dr John Symcotts wrote that the spread, progression, and 'expulsion' of smallpox naturally differed in men, women, and children due to 'an analogy requisite in that infection between the agent and patient, as likeness in age, sex, [and] temper'.[41] Sex and age could function as parallel—or, perhaps, conjoined—variables in assessing the manifestation, and the impact, of common illnesses.

[37] Dewhurst (ed.), *Willis's Oxford Casebook*, p. 152; James, *A Medicinal Dictionary*, vol. II, s.v. 'Fluor Albus' (citing Giorgio Baglivi, *De Praxi Medica Ad Priscam Observandi Rationem Revocanda. Libri Duo. Accedunt Dissertationes Novae* [Rome, 1696], Lib. 2, Cap. 8). John Astruc challenged the reliability of these diagnostic rules, asserting that they did not enable practitioners to accurately distinguish between gonorrhoea and the whites. See Astruc, *A Treatise of the Venereal Disease*, vol. I, pp. 266–8; Astruc, *A Treatise on all the Diseases*, pp. 136–41.

[38] Dewhurst, *Willis's Oxford Casebook*, p. 152.

[39] Thomas Sydenham, 'An Epistolary Discourse to the Learned Doctour William Cole, Concerning Some Observations of the Confluent Small-Pox, and of Hysterick Diseases', in *The Whole Works of that Excellent Practical Physician Dr Thomas Sydenham . . .*, trans. John Pechey (London, 1696), 404–78, p. 409.

[40] RCP 535 (Treatise on smallpox, with copies of letters and prescriptions, *circa* 1691), fols. 5r, 6v; Bodleian Library, MS Locke, fol. 119, p. 169 (5 September 1681) cited in Dewhurst (ed.), *Dr Thomas Sydenham*, p. 53; John Dunton (ed.), *Athenian Mercury*, 1 (21) (n.d., 1691), fol. *recto*, question 3; Sydenham, 'An Epistolary', p. 409.

[41] Poynter and Bishop (eds), *A Seventeenth-Century Doctor*, p. 18. For more on the gendered imbalance in the diagnosis, prevention, and treatment of venereal disease in early modern medicine, see W. Schleiner, 'Infection and Cure through Women: Renaissance Constructions of Syphilis', *Journal of Medieval and Renaissance Studies*, 24 (1994), 499–517; idem, 'Renaissance Moralizing about Syphilis and Prevention', in *Medical Ethics in the Renaissance* (Washington, DC, 1995), 162–202; K. Siena, 'Pollution, Promiscuity, and the Pox: English Venereology and the Early Modern Medical Discourse on Social and Sexual Danger', *Journal of the History of Sexuality*, 8 (1998), 553–74; idem, *Venereal Disease*.

III

It can be conclusively demonstrated that medical practice operated according to the notion that female physiology, and its associated functions, had a direct impact on the causation, transmission, manifestation, and cure of disease. According to the humoural theory which governed early modern medicine, women's sexual organs were internal because the female body was cold and moist; men's sexual organs were external because the male body was hot and dry. Excess moisture in the male body was effectively expelled through metabolic processes, excrement, or perspiration. On the other hand, the lack of heat inherent in the female constitution meant that there was a surplus of moisture which took the form of blood to nourish the foetus *in utero* or breast milk after childbirth. When a woman was neither pregnant nor lactating, this surplus was purged via menstruation. Regular menstrual cycles were viewed as nature's way of expelling the superfluous humours inherent in women and, hence, maintaining bodily health.[42] Seventeenth- and early eighteenth-century medical practitioners often associated an abatement of disease symptoms with menstruation because it represented a natural 'flux' through which the excess humours of the feminine constitution could be purged.[43]

Many years following her recovery from smallpox, Martha Andrews continued to experience sharp pain and 'sometymes a white webbe' in her eyes. During the 1640s, her physician, William Petty (1623–87), noted that '[w]hen her Courses went freely then the Rheume did less trouble her'.[44] One hundred years later, Richard Wilkes (1691–1760), a Wolverhampton physician, also observed that the malarial symptoms in one of his female patients subsided during her menstrual cycle, but returned soon thereafter. He remarked that '[t]he Bark always checkt the Fever, but every Month since then at the End of the Menstrual Flux, the same Symptoms return[ed] upon her, as at the first Seizsure.'[45]

Professional recognition of menstruation also appears to have impacted on the pattern of treatment in women. It was recommended that only after the patient's constitution was 'restor'd' should the practitioner attempt to regulate 'the Menstrual flux'.[46] After completing his remedy for 'a virulent Gonorrhea' in one

[42] Maclean, *The Renaissance Notion of Woman*, pp. 30–1, 36; P. Crawford, 'Attitudes to Menstruation in Seventeenth-Century England', *Past and Present*, 91 (1981), 47–73, pp. 50–3. Regarding premodern western medical theories of physiological sex differences and the role of menstruation in women's health, see Flemming, *Medicine and the Making of Roman Women*, pp. 119–22, 160–1, 310–13, 337–9; M. H. Green, 'The Transmission of Ancient Theories of Female Physiology and Disease through the Early Middle Ages' (unpublished Ph.D. thesis, Princeton University, 1985), pp. 40–7; idem (ed.), *The Trotula: A Medieval Compendium of Women's Medicine*, The Middle Ages Series (Philadelphia, 2001), pp. 19–22, 35–9; J. Cadden, *Meanings of Sex Difference in the Middle Ages: Medicine, Science, and Culture*, Cambridge History of Medicine (Cambridge and New York, 1993), esp. pp. 13–53, 169–227.

[43] See Wellcome 5005, p. 86; L. McCray Beier, *Sufferers and Healers: The Experience of Illness in Seventeenth-Century England* (London and New York, 1987), p. 123; BL Sl. 78 (Barker, M.D. of Shrewsbury, Observations on cases in physick, 1595–1605, fols. 155r – 89v), fol. 186r.

[44] BL Additional MS 72891 (Sir William Petty's notes relating to medical practice, *circa* 1645–76), fol. 271r.

[45] Wellcome 5005, p. 86.

female patient (characterized by a 'running' discharge and 'pain in her thise'), Alexander Morgan turned his efforts to curing her remaining vaginal discharge which 'did proseed from the w[h]ites[,] and she having a suppre[s]sion of her menses'.[47] Thus, the treatment administered by practitioners to their female clientele was dependent upon two important considerations: the primary disease symptoms and the condition of female-specific flows. These two components were inexorably intertwined.

Depending upon the circumstances, menstruation could be regarded as a cause, a symptom, or a cure.[48] Menstruation was, in fact, a double-edged sword in the medical diagnosis and treatment of women. On the one hand, it presented a physiological function through which humoural imbalance could be remedied. This was a unique, female-specific function that was unavailable to the male body. Although the curative properties of menstruation could be mimicked in male patients through either spontaneous or induced bleeding, particularly at the nose or haemorrhoidal veins, these processes were also available to women.[49] On the other hand, however, a disruption of menstruation due to medical intervention could lead to illness. In 1679, physician Thomas Trapham summarized this dualistic view in a publication which detailed the nature of illnesses in Jamaica. He argued that 'the Female [is] not wanting so much the evacuations, by bleeding especially, nor that by vomiting so generally, both which are almost necessary to the other sex ... nature providing better for the one than the other Sex by her great discharges of turgent humours'. Despite this 'natural' advantage, however, Trapham also asserted that '... Emeticks or opening of a Vein, may in the Female prevent or corrupt natures own intentions. ... Wherefore advertency is to be had, and that more cautious, concerning the more tender Sex su[i]table to their Nature, Time, Age and other circumstances'.[50] It appears, then, that the medical treatment of female patients was considered to be simultaneously advantaged and disadvantaged by their physiology.

Medical practitioners frequently expressed concern over disturbing menstruation in their female patients. It was believed that a change in the normal menstrual cycle resulted in illness because the body was not able to dispel the excess humours

[46] Wellcome 6888, fol. 12v; BL Sl. 78, fol. 166v. See also John Pechey, *A General Treatise of the Diseases of Maids, Big-Bellied Women, Child-Bed Women, and Widows* ... (London, 1696), p. 47.

[47] Wellcome 3631, pp. 21, 23.

[48] Wellcome 5005, p. 86; BL Sl. 78, fol. 186; Sloane, *A Voyage*, pp. ciii, civ, cx. See also Beier, *Sufferers and Healers*, p. 123; Crawford, 'Attitudes to Menstruation', pp. 50–4, 56; M. Stolberg, 'A Woman's Hell?: Medical Perceptions of Menopause in Preindustrial Europe', *Bulletin of the History of Medicine*, 73 (1999), 404–28, p. 408.

[49] BL Sl. 78, fol. 159v; RCP 535, fols. 8r, 11r; BL Sl. 1112 (Prescriptions made up by apothecaries, Cambridge, 1619–22, 1626–8, fols. 1–34), fols. 21r, 22v; Wellcome 6888, fols. 102–3r, 204; RCP 206/4, pp. 64 (Dr Carver, n.d.), 100 (Dr Carver, 15 July 1692); BL Sl. 1408, fol. 94r (rev.); Poynter and Bishop (eds), *A Seventeenth-Century Doctor*, p. 82; Ward and Yell (eds), *The Medical Casebook*, pp. 71–90; William Sermon, *The Ladies Companion, or the English Midwife* ... (London, 1671), pp. 168–74. See also Duden, *The Woman Beneath*, p. 116; Pomata, 'Menstruating Men', pp. 111–13, 123–30; J. L. Beusterien, 'Jewish Male Menstruation in Seventeenth-Century Spain', *Bulletin of the History of Medicine*, 73 (1999), 447–56; Smith, 'Women's Health Care', pp. 10–11, 42, 269 (n. 4).

[50] Thomas Trapham, *A Discourse of the State of Health in the Island of Jamaica* ... (London, 1679), p. 80.

inherent in women. Practitioners not only monitored the frequency, quantity, and quality of women's menstrual cycles, but they also prescribed medicines aimed at regulating these fluxes. In this way, menstruation operated as a general guide for female health and, at times, represented the principal tool in diagnosis and treatment, even taking precedence over symptoms of disease. For instance, despite a longstanding venereal ulceration on her face, Margaret Voy was deemed by Rutherford to be 'otherwise ... in perfect Health for she has had her Menses regularly'.[51] There existed no similar barometer by which practitioners could gauge the general physical condition of the male body. Although involuntary seminal emissions and painful erections could be signs of venereal disease in men, they were not assigned the same significance as menstruation.[52] For male patients, there was no equivalent sex-specific function that measured overall bodily health or treatment efficacy.

Practitioners not only noted the state of their female patients' vaginal discharges and menstrual cycles, but also adjusted the course of treatment based on this information. Extracts from a collection of late seventeenth-century practitioner consultation letters reveals that Sir Thomas Browne (1605–1710) had advised Dr Thomas Carver to treat the venereal ulcer on the nose of one woman by 'bleed[ing] her once or twice in the arm at due time as not to hinder her menses, and then at the jugulars or forehead vein by Leaches and then to consider whether we might not apply a Leach upon the part'.[53] In 1742, the possibility of sex-specific effects of cinchona were recognized by Wilkes, who continued to prescribe it to his female malarial patient only after determining that it did not disrupt her menstruation: 'As the Cort. Peruv. never checkt the menstrual Flux, I order'd her to take it as usual every 3 or 4 Hours beginning after the Flux had continued 48 Hours, till the Fever was stopt'.[54] Thus, in treating women, practitioners carefully considered the impact of their prescriptions on the female body, and altered their remedies as necessary. Aside from the possible exception of venereal disease, practitioners did not alter their prescriptions for male patients according to any such sex-specific physiological function. This appears to have been a consistent approach to treating patients for many afflictions throughout the seventeenth and early eighteenth centuries.

Pregnancy, like vaginal discharge and menstruation, was also afforded special consideration by practitioners. There were two main reasons for this concern: one was disease transmission, the other was the preservation of both the female

[51] Wellcome 6888, fol. 166r.

[52] BL Sl. 275 (Stephen Bredwell, Physician of London, Diarium practicum, 1592–1607), fol. 101r; BL Sl. 153 (Joseph Binns' casebook, 1633–63), fol. 251v; RCP 206/4, p. 145 (Dr Carver, 21 June 1697); Wellcome 3631, pp. 54–6, n.p. (24 August 1725–10 October 1725).

[53] RCP 206/4, pp. 31–2 (Dr Carver, n.d.). This practitioner is only identified as 'Dr Carver' in the manuscript. However, it is probably Thomas Carver (d. 1708), of Suffolk, who received his MD from Cambridge in 1670. See J. Venn and J. A. Venn, *Alumni Cantabrigienses: A Biographical List of All Known Students, Graduates and Holders of Office at the University of Cambridge, from the Earliest Times to 1900*, 10 vols, 2 Pts, vol. I, Pt I (Cambridge, 1922), p. 304.

[54] Wellcome 5005, pp. 86–7.

patient and her unborn child. Early modern medical theory held that there was a sympathy or 'translation of the Matter' between the female breasts and the womb.[55] Practitioners believed that, during pregnancy, disease could be transmitted to a foetus through the mother's suppressed menstrual blood.[56] As explained above, the underlying rationale was that this superfluous blood nourished the baby while *in utero* (which explained the disruption of regular menstrual cycles during pregnancy). Following delivery, it was thought to be diverted and expelled from the body as lochial discharge and breast milk.[57] Thus, pregnancy was viewed as one way that common illnesses could be conveyed by the female body. Practitioners frequently treated children whom they believed had acquired *lues venerea* from their infected mothers.[58] It was also widely held that the 'Original Cause' of smallpox was transmitted during pregnancy through 'the Impurity of the Menstrual Blood'. The appearance of smallpox pustules was regarded as the method through which the body's natural heat expelled these in-bred impurities.[59] Although practitioners believed that certain illnesses, including gout, could be inherited through the seminal properties of the father, there is no evidence that this resulted in closer monitoring of disease symptoms or an alteration of prescription, as it did in the treatment of women.[60]

For many practitioners, pregnancy also evoked a more cautious approach to treatment. It was feared that pregnant women who contracted diseases such as

[55] Anonymous, *An Account of the Causes of Some Particular Rebellious Distempers* ... (London?, 1670), p. 23.

[56] Thomas Phaire, *The Boke of Chyldren* (London, 1553; repr. edn, Edinburgh and London, 1957), p. 57; Robert Pemell, *De Morbis Puerorum, or, A Treatise of the Diseases of Children* ... (London, 1653; repr. edn, Tuckahoe, NY, 1971), p. 21; Dunton (ed.), *Athenian Mercury*, 2 (5) (Tuesday, 9 June 1691), fol. *verso*, question 18; Willis, *The London Practice*, p. 622; Sloane, *A Voyage*, pp. cxx–cxxi; BL Sl. 4025 (Correspondence of Sir Hans Sloane), fols. 122–3 (William Derham to Sloane, 7 October 1713).

[57] Although various aspects of this theory had begun to undergo questioning by the late seventeenth century, the notion that there was consent (if not a direct link) between the womb and breasts continued until at least the mid-eighteenth century. See Anonymous, *An Account*, pp. 22–3; Jane Sharp, *The Midwives Book* ... (London, 1671; repr. edn, New York and London, 1985), pp. 254, 267–8; RCP 504 (Collection of medical receipts, *circa* 1690s), n.p. (citing Thomas Gibson, *The Anatomy of Humane Bodies Epitomized* ... [London, 1682], p. 228); Sloane, *A Voyage*, p. cii; Pechey, *A General Treatise*, pp. 19–20, 88–9, 173–4, 179; Wellcome 6888, fols. 9v – 10v, 101r – 3r, 104r, 204r; Astruc, *A Treatise on all the Diseases*, pp. 423–5. For further discussion, see V. Fildes, *Wet Nursing: A History from Antiquity to the Present*, Family, Sexuality, and Social Relations in Past Times (Oxford and New York, 1988), p. 9; idem, *Breasts, Bottles and Babies: A History of Infant Feeding* (Edinburgh, 1986), pp. 180–1; P. Crawford, '"The Sucking Child": Adult Attitudes to Child Care in the First Year of Life in Seventeenth-Century England', *Continuity and Change*, 1 (1986), 23–52, p. 30; idem, 'Attitudes to Menstruation', pp. 50–2; Eccles, 'Development and Birth of the Foetus', in *Obstetrics and Gynaecology*, 43–57, pp. 51–3.

[58] Sloane, *A Voyage*, pp. cxx–i. For the argument that children born to parents with *lues venerea* were more prone to smallpox, see RCP 535, fol. 6v.

[59] Dunton (ed.), *Athenian Mercury*, 2 (5) (Tuesday, 9 June 1691), fol. *verso*, question 18. See also Pemell, *De Morbis Puerorum*, p. 21; Willis, *The London Practice*, p. 622.

[60] RCP 206/4, p. 59 ([Dr Carver], 16 June 1679); Sydenham, 'Of the Gout', in *The Whole Works*, 481–525, pp. 482, 489; Willis, *The London Practice*, pp. 503–4. For more on the hereditary role of the masculine seed in other diseases, see RCP 206/4, p. 3 (Dr Budgen, n.d.); BL Sl. 4034 (Correspondence of Sir Hans Sloane), fol. 242r (Mrs B. Boyle to Sloane, 9 October [n.d.]); Wellcome 6919, fol. 15 (observations 45 and 46); Dunton (ed.), *Athenian Mercury*, 1 (18) (Saturday, 23 May 1691), question 5, fol. *verso*. See also R. Porter, 'The Ruin of the Constitution: The Early Interpretation of Gout', *Transactions of the Medical Society of London*, 110 (1995), 90–103, see esp. pp. 91–2, 94, 98–100.

smallpox were in particular danger of miscarrying due to the impoverished state of their blood.[61] In such instances, practitioners often avoided administering prescriptions containing ingredients that could inadvertently function as uterine stimulants.[62] In 1728, Mrs Andrews, nine months pregnant and ill with an ague, was administered cinchona only after other remedies, including bloodletting and anodyne pills, had failed to elicit a cure.[63] The anonymous Scottish practitioner who treated her noted in his casebook that he had prescribed cinchona to remove the fever as a last resort because 'her strength was so much wasted'.[64] In cases of pregnancy, medical practitioners proceeded cautiously, weighing the risks of treatment against the dangers of allowing the illness to continue. Pregnancy also had a direct impact on prescription. For example, one pregnant woman was prescribed an unusually large amount of cinchona, seven ounces, before there was a noticeable abatement in her malarial symptoms.[65] Her practitioner explained that '[p]erhaps she relapst the oft[e]ner because she was with Child, during which time the Blood is seldom good and Diseases frequently obstinate'.[66] In many instances, practitioners began by prescribing pregnant women gentler remedies and smaller dosages than administered to other patients, but, if unsuccessful, later altered them in order to elicit a 'cure'.

Lactation was yet another female 'flux' which received special attention from practitioners in their treatment of venereal disease, smallpox, and malaria. It was believed that the humoural quality of breast milk could be corrupted by disease. Rutherford explained that intermittent fevers produced unhealthy changes in both the blood and the breast milk 'by causing a viscidity and L[e]ntor which by means of the hot fit is attenuated and sent out of the Body'.[67] Like pregnancy, lactation was considered to be a vehicle of disease transmission. In 1688, Sloane had urged two female malarial patients to wean their suckling infants because he believed that disease could be communicated in this manner. Moreover, he feared that failing to do so could prove harmful to the nursing women themselves due to the compromised, 'perhaps not very healthy', quality of their breast milk.[68] Practitioners were cautious about treating lactating women for reasons other than disease transmission and progression. They also worried about the possible effects of their prescribed treatments on both the mother and the child. While Sloane prescribed cinchona to his male patients and menstruating female patients as soon as a fever had established itself as malarial, he administered it to a nursing mother only after several courses of vomits and

[61] RCP 535, fol. 6v. Due to their weak constitutions, children were also singled out as another high-risk group; see fol. 7r.

[62] Ibid., fol. 6v.

[63] Wellcome 7501, fols. 5r, 23r.

[64] Ibid., fol. 23v.

[65] Ibid., fol. 55v. Practitioners normally prescribed between half an ounce and three ounces. See also RCP 206/4, p. 92 (Dr Carver, 18 September 1691); RCP 513, p. 35; BL Sl. 1589, fols. 306v(rev.) – 5r(rev.); Sloane, *A Voyage*, p. cxxxiv.

[66] Wellcome 7501, fol. 55v. For the perceived effects that cinchona had upon the blood, see Wellcome 6919, fol. 31r.

[67] Wellcome 6888, fol. 15v.

[68] Sloane, *A Voyage*, pp. cxxxi–ii, cxxxvii.

'sweaters' had failed to relieve her symptoms.[69] Similarly, he also chose to treat a non-menstruating woman with alternative remedies prior to prescribing cinchona, presumably due to his uncertainty over whether or not she was pregnant.[70]

IV

It appears, then, that common diseases were routinely believed to possess different manifestations and to require different treatment regimens in the male and the female body. Although vaginal discharge, menstruation, pregnancy, and lactation were steeped in the same humoural theory as the male body, the unique, female-specific nature of these functions permitted, and required, medical practitioners to perceive and treat women outside of any supposed one-sex model. The evidence pertaining to early modern British medical practice contradicts Laqueur's argument that, prior to the late eighteenth century, medicine was premised upon a one-sex (male) model of the body. Indeed, it points in the opposite direction. In fact, there were even some practitioners who appear to have conceptualized the body according to a female-centric paradigm. One such practitioner was the Edinburgh physician, Archibald Pitcairn (1652–1713), who attempted to explain perceived differences between the flow of blood in female and male bodies by confidently asserting that 'a Man is a Woman without a Womb. Therefore the Blood runs in greater Quantity to the lower Parts of Women, than those of Men &c.'[71] It should be noted that Pitcairn was not alone in drawing such conclusions regarding the centrality of the female body to seventeenth-century medical theory. Estelle Cohen has pointed out that the Cartesian philosopher, François Poullain de la Barre, in his *De l'égalité des deux sexes* (translated into English in 1677), reversed Aristotelian theory by asserting the plausibility of arguing that men were imperfect women.[72]

During the seventeenth and early eighteenth centuries, the medical treatment of common illnesses was influenced by the fact that medical practitioners conceptualized the female body as capable of manifesting, transmitting, and responding to disease and treatment in ways that the male body could not. Women were considered to be distinct from men due to their unique physiological constitution and associated internal 'flows'. Practitioners also inquired about the state of

[69] Ibid., pp. xci, xcix–c, cvii, cxiii–iv, cxxxi–ii, cxxxiv, cxxxvi–vii, cxlvii, cxlix.

[70] Ibid., p. cx. For a detailed discussion of the ambiguity and uncertainty expressed by medical practitioners about the signs of pregnancy, see McClive, 'The Hidden Truths of the Belly'.

[71] Archibald Pitcairn, *The Whole Works of Dr. Archibald Pitcairn . . .*, trans. George Sewell and J. T. Desaguliers, 2nd edn (London, 1727), p. 235. This work was originally published in Latin as *Dissertationes Medicae* (Rotterdam, 1701). All English translations were published posthumously; Pitcairn died in 1713. Recently, scholars have begun to present women as the early modern normative model in cases of bleeding, largely due to menstruation. See Pomata, 'Menstruating Men', pp. 112–13; Beusterien, 'Jewish Male Menstruation', pp. 447–56.

[72] E. Cohen, '"What the Women at All Times Would Laugh At": Redefining Equality and Difference, *circa* 1660–1760', *Osiris*, 2nd ser., 12 (1997), 121–42, pp. 135–7. Eve Keller has also argued that Jane Sharp similarly challenged the male-centric medical model. See E. Keller, 'Mrs Jane Sharp: Midwifery and the Critique of Medical Knowledge in Seventeenth-Century England', *Women's Writing: The Elizabethan to Victorian Period*, 2 (1995), 101–19.

female physiological functions, even in cases of *non*-female-specific illnesses. Although practitioners aimed to obtain the same data about female patients as male patients—age of patient, length of illness, symptoms of illness, quantity and quality of urine and excrement, and previous medical treatment—they also sought quantitative (i.e. pattern, duration, amount) and qualitative (i.e. colour, density, degree of pain) information regarding the female-specific functions of menstruation, vaginal discharge, pregnancy, and lactation.[73] This signifies the existence of a sexed model of treatment wherein the female body stood alongside the male body.

When considering the usefulness of the sexed model to the study of early modern British medicine, it is important to remember that practitioners treated real patients who presented a variety of symptoms in the context of a specific constitution. Several variables were recognized as forming the foundation of successful treatment. These included the categories of constitution, age, and sex. For the practitioner, these variables clearly overlapped and, in many cases, reinforced each other. Thus, the question for the historian is, to what extent are generalizations based on a sexed model of theory and practice either possible or desirable?

In respect to treatment, practitioners clearly approached the adult body as a 'sexed' body. The female constitution had to be treated differently than that of the male constitution because, as we have seen, the consequences for bodily health were different. Even for diseases that on the surface appeared to have possessed no gendered component,[74] adult women had to be treated differently. The evidence does not simply suggest that men were regarded as the normative and women as derivations from this norm. It would appear that women of menstruating, childbearing age were conceived as distinct not only from adult males, but from all other patients, including pre-pubescent children and post-menopausal women.

V

Differences in medical treatment were determined by the patient's age, a variable that was intricately tied to the physiological changes within the sexed body. While a consideration of the evidence pertaining to pre-pubescent patients can prove fruitful here, it should be noted that it is also inherently limited due to the difficulty in determining whether the differences in treatments were due to sex or age

[73] BL Sl. 79, fol. 153r; BL Sl. 275, fols. 10v, 18, 20v, 22v, 24r, 30v, 42r, 48r, 64v, 83r; RCP 641, pp. 53, 63, 68, 135, 138; Wellcome 6888, fols. 165, 166r, 204; BL Sl. 78, fols. 166v, 168r, 172r, 179v, 181r, 186; RCP 206/4, pp. 54 (Dr Carver, 4 October 1677), 73–4 (Dr Carver to [Dr Edward Hulse], 25 May 1691); Wellcome 5005, pp. 37–8, 43; Wellcome 5006, pp. 6, 59–60, 125; Dewhurst (ed.), *Willis's Oxford Casebook*, pp. 79–80, 90, 98, 101, 124, 147, 149, 151; Bishop and Poynter (eds), *A Seventeenth-Century Doctor*, pp. 70, 86; Sloane, *A Voyage*, p. civ; Ward and Yell (eds), *The Medical Casebook*, pp. 95–6, 102–5. See also Samuel Auguste Tissot, *Advice to People in General, with Respect to their Health*. . ., 2 vols, vol. II (Edinburgh, 1768), pp. 326–9.

[74] Although this article has focused more explicitly on the 'sexed' rather than the 'gendered' dimensions of medical diagnosis and treatment, these processes were implicitly 'gendered' by the manner in which the 'sexed' body (and its physiology) influenced the medical response of practitioners to male and female patients who were afflicted with the same diseases.

(and their correlation to body size and strength for the purposes of dosage and potency). The impression thus far, however, is that any differences contained in the records pertaining to pre-pubescent patients were likely more due to age than sex.

A survey of seventeenth-century medical casebooks indicates that patients whose sex was left unspecified by practitioners overwhelmingly constituted children under the age of ten.[75] For these patients, sex must have been largely immaterial for treatment regardless of the symptoms or ailments presented. The evidence reveals that practitioners, in instances where age was recorded, tended towards more precise recording of ages of infant and pre-pubescent children than was true for adolescents and adults, for whom more approximate ages were often recorded. This appears to have been due to the fact that body size helped to determine dosages and so the younger the patient, the greater the precision. Thus the medical treatment of pre-pubescent patients, by virtue of their undeveloped constitutions, rested more upon differences in age and corresponding body size than the notion of sexed physiology.[76] It was believed that, prior to reaching sexual maturity, children were free from certain diseases, such as gout, due to their unsexed constitutions. For instance, a seventeenth-century medical collection, citing a Hippocratic aphorism, held that '[a] boy is very rarely troubled with the Gout till hee hath used venery'.[77] The transition from the unsexed, pre-pubescent body to the sexed, physically mature body was marked by breast development and menarche in girls, and facial hair, testicular swellings, and vocal changes in boys.[78] Whereas children were believed to lack 'seed', these

[75] See Sloane, *A Voyage*, pp. c, cii, cix, cxxx, cxxxvii, cxlvii; Wellcome 7501, fols. 21v – 2r (both feminine and masculine pronouns were used to identify this child), 25r; Wellcome 3631, p. 11 (this represents the only patient of unknown sex in this casebook). There are at least ten such cases (representing all the patients of unknown sex) in Nicholas Gaynsford's notebook for 1712–3. See Wellcome 6919, fols. 2r (observation 1), 2v (observations 3 and 4), 7v (observation 20), 12r (observation 38), 17v (unnumbered observation), 22r (unnumbered observation), 25v (unnumbered observation), 28r (unnumbered observation), 33v (unnumbered observation). All three patients of unknown sex are children in RCP 5, n.p. (these three instances included one case of a bubo and two cases of hernias). In George Bate's (1608–69) record of prescriptions, all six patients of undeterminable sex are children. See RCP 893 (George Bate's medical casebook, 1654–60), fols. 35r, 37r, 46v, 69v, 76r, 81v. In Edward Browne's (1644–1708) prescription book, eight of the eighteen patients of undeterminable sex were children. See BL Sl. 1865 (Prescription book of Dr Edward Browne, 18 October 1675 to 29 June 1678, fols. 62–98), fols. 65v – 6v, 68v, 84, 85r, 86v, 91v, 93v, 95r.

[76] RCP 206/4, pp. 117 ([Dr Wench], n.d.), 148 (Dr Carver, 6 September 1697; Dr Carver, 13 September 1697); RCP 535, fol. 7r; Wellcome 6919, fols. 25v – 6r; Sloane, *A Voyage*, pp. civ–v, cxv, cxxiii; Bishop and Poynter (eds), *A Seventeenth-Century Doctor*, pp. 19, 97; Walter Harris, *An Exact Enquiry Into, and Cure of the Acute Diseases of Infants...*, trans. William Cockburn (London, 1693), pp. 2–4; Pemell, *De Morbis Puerorum*, pp. 2, 4–6, 9–10, 25, 30–1, 39, 46–7, 51, 54–5, 59, 64, 66; Phaire, *The Boke of Chyldren*, pp. 28–30, 32, 34, 36–7, 45, 47, 50, 52–4, 60; M. Repetski, 'The Emergence of Childhood Medicine in Early Modern England' (unpublished seminar paper, McMaster University, Hamilton, Ontario, April 2003), pp. 9–10.

[77] RCP 513, p. 63. See also Sydenham, 'Of the Gout', pp. 481–2, 489. Hippocratic authors had attributed gout to sexual virility (or excess). For instance, see R. Porter and G. S. Rousseau, *Gout: The Patrician Malady* (New Haven, 1998), pp. 14–15, 23, 26–7.

[78] Harvey, 'The Substance of Sexual Difference', pp. 214–15; Flemming, *Medicine and the Making of Roman Women*, pp. 236–7, 310–11, 313. For more on pre-modern views regarding puberty,

physiological changes were interpreted as signals of sexually mature, sexed bodies. It appears that once the patient reached sexual maturity, there was an ascribed, or at least an assumed, difference between the bodily constitutions of men and women. Moreover, the physiological changes that accompanied ageing in the sexed female body, notably menarche and menopause, directly impacted upon the medical treatment of common illnesses which, at first glance, appeared to have no sex-specific elements.

A number of diseases, however, were clearly ascribed age-specific, in addition to sex-specific, attributes. These included dropsy and gout. Dropsy was regarded as rarely afflicting men who 'seem to be vigourous and strong, in the Prime of their Age'.[79] It was, however, believed to commonly strike 'weak People', especially non-menstruating (including those who were pregnant or post-menopausal) or barren women, and, less frequently, children and elderly men.[80] On the other hand, male patients were thought to be the most susceptible to gout. The only instances of 'true and genuine Gout' in women were believed to strike those who were 'old, or of a Masculine habit of Body.'[81] One seventeenth-century collection of medical remedies, citing a Hippocratic aphorism, noted that '[a] woman is not troubled with the Gout, unlesse her monthly terms faile her'.[82] This aetiology appears to have been based upon empirical observation. Gout is, in fact, a disease that chiefly afflicts middle-aged men and post-menopausal women.[83] It is interesting—and compelling of further research—that, while post-menopausal-aged women rarely appear amongst the extant case records for venereal disease, smallpox, and malaria,[84] they are located more frequently in cases of gout (which was regarded as a nervous disorder).[85] According to the humoural paradigm, through the process of ageing, the body grew colder and

especially in regard to female physiology, see H. King, *The Disease of Virgins: Green Sickness, Chlorosis and the Problems of Puberty* (London and New York, 2004).

[79] Wellcome 7501, fol. 33v.

[80] Ibid., fols. 33v – 4r (quotation on fol. 34r); Sydenham, 'Of a Dropsie', in *The Whole Works*, 525–46, pp. 525–7; Willis, *The London Practice*, p. 507; BL Sl. 79, fol. 123r; RCP 513, p. 63.

[81] Sydenham, 'Of the Gout', pp. 481, 489–90. For more on the history of gender differences ascribed to gout, see T. G. Benedek, 'Gout in Women: A Historical Perspective', *Bulletin of the History of Medicine*, 71 (1997), 1–22; Porter and Rousseau, *Gout*, pp. 5, 13, 15, 22–3, 180–1; Flemming, *Medicine and the Making of Roman Women*, pp. 159, 160 (n. 81).

[82] RCP 513, p. 63.

[83] T. G. Benedek, 'Part VIII: Major Human Diseases Past and Present, Section VIII. 63: Gout', in K. F. Kiple *et al.*, (eds), *The Cambridge World History of Human Disease* (Cambridge and New York, 1993), 763–72, p. 764.

[84] BL Sl. 275, fols. 11v – 12r; RCP 625, unfoliated prescriptions dated 18 September 1723, 10 December 1723; Wellcome 1110 (Memorandum Book of Dr George Bayly, of Chichester, 1716–57), pp. 101–2.

[85] BL Sl. 1112, fol. 21v; RCP 6 (Samuel England, notebook containing prescriptions and case notes, 1730–3), pp. 394–6, 400; BL Sl. 4078 (Correspondence of Sir Hans Sloane), fols. 206r – 7v (Thomas Peplow, Apothecary of Market Drayton, co. Salop., to Sir Hans Sloane, 17 October 1739); Willis, *The Practice of Physick*, p. 502; Sydenham, 'Of the Gout', pp. 488–90; RCP 6, p. 388. See also A. Guerrini, *Obesity and Depression in the Enlightenment: The Life and Times of George Cheyne*, Oklahoma Project for Discourse and Theory, Series for Science and Culture, III (Norman, OK, 2000), pp. 103, 105. Diagnoses of palsy and apoplexy were also associated with older persons, including women, in the treatise and manuscript sources. For instance, see Willis, *The London Practice of Physick*, pp. 441–4, 451; BL Sl. 1589, fol. 294r; RCP 513, p. 64; BL Sl. 79, fols.

drier.[86] In part, this explained to early modern physicians why older women eventually ceased to menstruate and, hence, why they were portrayed as more analogous to men, at least in cases of gout, which was viewed primarily as a male-specific disease.[87] Regardless of the intrinsic complexities, it is clear that diagnosis and treatment of adult patients hinged upon the inter-connected variables of sex and age.

VI

In conclusion, an examination of how men and women were treated for venereal disease, smallpox, and malaria reveals that seventeenth- and early eighteenth-century British medicine did not employ a one-sex model of the body in practice. Because practitioners based their treatment upon a recognition of the physiological differences between bodies—including the child, the adult male, the menstruating female, and the 'aged'—it is inaccurate to state that the adult male body was regarded as the normative, or the superior, medical model. Rather than adhering to a one-sex or male-centred model, early modern medicine held a multi-faceted approach that accounted for significant differences, including those of sex and age. These were inter-dependent, and each bore an important relationship to bodily constitution. A medical practitioner could not, and did not, treat his patients only according to the category of 'sex'. Instead, the holistic nature of the patient model allowed and required similarities and differences to co-exist in the treatment of men and women. It simultaneously incorporated biological differences and upheld the humoural theory of medicine. Moreover, while this appears to have been a consistent component of medical practice throughout Britain during the period *circa* 1600–1740, it does not appear to have been restricted to this particular time and place. Indeed, although similar analyses for other periods and regions have yet to be written, it seems reasonable to suggest that sex (and age) differences were central aspects of diagnosis and treatment throughout the entire pre-modern western tradition of medicine.[88]

Although it has been argued that sexual difference was a matter merely of degree in theory, it was certainly a matter of essential difference in practice.

123r, 135v (Barker appears to have grouped gout, palsy, and apoplexy together as common diagnoses for 'weak' or 'old' bodies); RCP 206/4, p. 52 ([Dr Carver], 8 September 1685).

[86] G. J. Gruman, *A History of Ideas About the Prolongation of Life: The Evolution of Prolongevity Hypotheses to 1800*, Transactions of the American Philosophical Society, new ser., vol. LVI, Pt IX (Philadelphia, December 1966; repr. edn, New York, 1977), pp. 16, 60, 64, 71; L. Botelho, 'Old Age and Menopause in Rural Women in Early Modern Suffolk', in L. A. Botelho and P. Thane (eds), *Women and Ageing in British Society Since 1500*, Women and Men in History (Harlow and New York, 2001), 43–65, pp. 52–3; L. A. Dean-Jones, *Women's Bodies in Classical Greek Science* (Oxford and New York, 1994), pp. 105–9.

[87] See Botelho, 'Old Age', p. 52; Dean-Jones, *Women's Bodies*, p. 107.

[88] The centrality of sex and age differences within pre-modern medical theory has been briefly addressed, especially with regard to Hippocratic and Galenic texts, in Green, 'The Transmission of Ancient Theories'; idem (ed.), *The Trotula*; Flemming, *Medicine and the Making of Roman Women*; King, *The Disease of Virgins*; D. Jacquart and C. Thomasset, *Sexuality and Medicine in the Middle Ages*, trans. M. Adamson (Cambridge, 1988); Cadden, *Meanings of Sex Difference*.

The sexed body was not an innovation of the late eighteenth century. Indeed, the evidence from British medical practice for the period 1600–1740 provides no support for a one-sex model or even for a straightforward, linear progression towards the two-sex model. While it is true that some practitioners made obvious dualistic contrasts (such as Pitcairn's comment that a man was essentially a woman without a uterus), many practitioners readily acknowledged the interconnections between constitution, age, and sex. In considering the sexed body, it is always seductive to play the female off the male or *vice versa*. While Simone de Beauvoir famously asserted that, throughout history, woman was the 'other' man,[89] any attempt to make such a claim would be futile and unrepresentative of the complexity of early modern British medicine.

Acknowledgements

Early versions of this paper were presented to the Department of History, McMaster University, 18 March 2003, and the Society for the Social History of Medicine's Summer Conference, Manchester, UK, 13 July 2003. This article has greatly benefited from the generous feedback provided by Dr J. D. Alsop and Dr G. Hudson, as well as the financial support of McMaster University, Memorial University of Newfoundland/Government of Newfoundland and Labrador, and the Social Sciences and Humanities Research Council of Canada Doctoral Fellowship. I am also grateful for the helpful suggestions provided by the two anonymous referees for *Social History of Medicine.*

[89] S. de Beauvoir, *The Second Sex*, trans. and ed. H. M. Parshley (New York, 1952; repr. edn, New York, 1964), pp. v, vi, xvi–viii, xxi–iii, xxv, xxix–x, 32–3, 48–9, 718. For discussion of how de Beauvoir contributed to the discussion of 'otherness' in gender history, see L. Jordanova, *Sexual Visions: Images of Gender in Science and Medicine between the Eighteenth and Twentieth Centuries*, Science and Literature (Madison, 1989), pp. 14–15.

Social History of Medicine Vol. 18 No. 1 © *The Society for the Social History of Medicine 2005, all rights reserved.*
doi:10.1093/sochis/hki004

'The True Assistant to the Obstetrician': State Regulation and the Legal Protection of Midwives in Nineteenth-Century Prussia

By ARLEEN MARCIA TUCHMAN*

SUMMARY. In recent years, historians of eighteenth- and nineteenth-century European midwifery have drawn attention to the great differences between midwives' experiences in England and the United States, where obstetricians succeeded by and large in displacing female practitioners, and midwives' experiences on the continent, where their fate was far more varied. While some countries witnessed the decline of midwives, in many others they were licensed and integrated into a government-sanctioned medical hierarchy. Scholars have disagreed, however, on how to evaluate the government's role in regulating midwives. Some have been critical, portraying midwives as victims of an alliance between the State and elite physicians who sought to place all other practitioners under their control. Others have cast midwives as beneficiaries of the State's protectionist policies, emphasizing their success in withstanding physicians' attempts to eliminate them entirely. Whilst these different interpretative models may reflect some regional variations, this article suggests that, in many cases, midwives both lost and won simultaneously: as State employees they lost much of their independence, but in exchange they gained protection not only from elite physicians, but also from unlicensed practitioners, who posed every bit as much of a threat.

KEYWORDS: midwifery, licensing, swaddling women, obstetrics, Prussia, Berlin, nineteenth century, State regulation.

Our understanding of the history of midwifery has been shaped largely by our knowledge of events in England and the United States. The standard picture is, accordingly, one in which male-midwives began as early as the eighteenth century to encroach upon a traditionally female domain, trying to usurp the place of the female midwife, who had managed childbirth in the company of other women for thousands of years. In the past decade, however, several historians of European midwifery have challenged, in Mary Lindemann's words, the 'tyranny of an Anglo-Saxon model', demonstrating its poor fit with developments on the continent.[1] Some have emphasized the absence of male-midwives from many European countries until well into the nineteenth century; others have focused on the far more active role of State and municipal authorities in regulating medical affairs. What is perhaps most telling is the large number of cities and towns on the continent where government officials stepped in to regulate the midwife's responsibilities and practices, licensing her rather than orchestrating

* Associate Professor of History, Vanderbilt University, History Department, Box 1802-B, Nashville, TN 37235, USA. E-mail: *arleen.m.tuchman@vanderbilt.edu*

[1] The quotation is from M. Lindemann, 'Professionals? Sisters? Rivals? Midwives in Braunschweig, 1750–1800', in H. Marland (ed.), *The Art of Midwifery. Early Modern Midwives in Europe* (London, 1993), 176–91, p. 176.

or even tolerating her decline. This was the case, for example, in certain parts of northern Italy, the Netherlands, and the German states.[2]

How one should evaluate the measures that defined and policed the duties of the midwife is, however, far from simple. The increased intrusion of government officials into the education of midwives contributed powerfully to a redefinition of the responsibilities of the midwife, severely limiting her realm of expertise. Yet, in many European countries, State licensing also protected midwives—at least those who were formally trained—allowing them to defend their turf when competition arose. So, did midwives gain or lose by the State's gradual encroachment into medical affairs? The answer may very well depend upon the region under question, for what is most noticeable about European developments in the eighteenth and nineteenth centuries is the great variation not only from state to state, but often from city to city as well. Nevertheless, historians of midwifery have tended to narrow their interpretative frameworks to one of two models, either emphasizing midwives' disappearance and thus their victimization, or their integration and thus their empowerment. They have done this despite the growing number of empirical studies that suggest a far more ambiguous model, one in which midwives were neither victims nor winners, but rather licensed practitioners, who paid a price for the protection they received.[3]

This more ambiguous model certainly applies to the situation in Brandenburg-Prussia, where the State began in the seventeenth century to weave a web of control over the practice of medicine. Although the responsibilities and regulations concerning midwives were only loosely stipulated at this time, over the years they were spelled out in ever greater detail. As a result, by the nineteenth century, when midwives in the city of Berlin began confronting serious competition from both unlicensed practitioners and from physicians who wished to

[2] See H. Marland, 'Introduction', in Marland (ed.), *The Art of Midwifery*, 1–8; M. E. Wiesner, 'The Midwives of South Germany and the Public/Private Dichotomy', in ibid., pp. 77–94; N. M. Filippini, 'The Church, the State and Childbirth: The Midwife in Italy During the Eighteenth Century', in ibid., pp. 152–75; Lindemann, 'Professionals?'; Marland, 'The "*burgerlijke*" Midwife: The *Stadsvroedvrouw* of Eighteenth-Century Holland', in ibid., pp. 192–213. See also F. Loetz, *Vom Kranken zum Patienten. "Medikalisierung" und medizinische Vergesellschaftung am Beispiel Badens 1750–1850* (Stuttgart, 1993), pp. 144–9, 182–90; A. Wilson, *The Making of Man-midwifery. Childbirth in England, 1660–1770* (Cambridge, MA, 1995); H. Marland and A. M. Rafferty (eds), *Midwives, Society and Childbirth. Debates and Controversies in the Modern Period* (London, 1997); M. Lindemann, *Health and Healing in Eighteenth-century Germany* (Baltimore, 1996), p. 194. In the United States, some state governments also instituted legislation concerning midwives in the last decades of the nineteenth century. The state of Wisconsin, for example, to some extent because of its large population of German immigrants, began licensing and regulating midwives in the 1870s. In Massachusetts, on the other hand, the government stepped in not to regulate, but rather to outlaw midwifery practice. See C. G. Borst, 'The Training and Practice of Midwives: A Wisconsin Study', in J. W. Leavitt (ed.), *Women and Health in America. Historical Readings*, 2nd edn (Wisconsin, 1999), 425–43. For another example in which state encroachment resulted in the demise of midwifery, see S. L. Smith, 'Medicine, Midwifery, and the State: Japanese Americans and Health Care in Hawai'i, 1885–1945', *Journal of Asian American Studies*, 4 (2001), 57–75.

[3] See, especially, Filippini, 'The Church, the State and Childbirth'; Lindemann, 'Professionals?'; Marland, 'The "*burgerlijke*" Midwife'; Loetz, *Vom Kranken zum Patienten*, pp. 144–9. Because each of their interests lies elsewhere, none of the authors draws out the implications of her study in the way I am doing here.

extend their area of expertise to childbirth, they were in a position to fight for the rights they had earned, albeit rights that had been curtailed over the years.

This article begins with a brief overview of the measures adopted by the Prussian government, beginning in the late seventeenth century, to educate and license midwives. It then turns to an in-depth analysis of a heated battle that took place in mid-nineteenth-century Berlin over the midwife's legitimate domain of practice. At issue was whether the midwife was, as the government sanctioned textbook on midwifery claimed, 'the true assistant to the obstetrician'.[4] The question had arisen because physicians, in an attempt to displace midwives, were employing swaddling women (*Wickelfrauen*) rather than midwives as their assistants, despite the fact that swaddling women were not officially part of the State medical hierarchy. The situation in Berlin was, to be sure, unusual; elsewhere in Prussia, midwives' control of uncomplicated births remained uncontested.[5] (Physicians had long been granted responsibility for complicated births.) In the capital, however, the presence of a university that encouraged the development of obstetrics as a research field, coupled with the high concentration of medical practitioners, all competing for the patronage of middle- and upper-class families, fostered an early challenge to the traditional division of labour. The Berlin physicians were not, however, successful. In the battle that ensued, midwives fought back by taking advantage of their legally-protected status, registering complaints with the city magistrates and insisting that the medical statutes, which spelled out their rights and responsibilities, be enforced. Thus, unlike in England and the United States, Prussian midwives had recourse to a legal system that offered them protection, and it was a system that they did not hesitate to use. In the end, however, what they fought for and won was the right to be the true 'assistant' to the obstetrician, clearly marking a loss of what had once been their sole domain.

The Regulation and Education of Midwives in Brandenburg-Prussia, 1685–1840

As early as 1685, Brandenburg-Prussia passed a medical edict that defined who could legitimately provide health care, regulated the qualifications of these practitioners, and created a health board (*Collegium medicum*) to do the policing. Section 18 of the edict dealt specifically with midwives, integrating them into a medical hierarchy at the same time that it placed limitations on the extent of their practice. Thereafter, anyone wishing to practise midwifery in Prussia had to be examined either by the *Collegium* or by a physician who had already been

[4] A new government-sanctioned textbook on midwifery, issued in the 1840s, charged the midwife to be 'the true assistant to the obstetrician'. This was mentioned in a report from the department of police, which was investigating charges that swaddling women were encroaching upon the rights of midwives. See Geheimes Staatsarchiv, Preussisches Kulturministerium, Rep. 76VIIIA, Nr. 882, Police Headquarters (*Polizei-Präsidium*) to the Minister of Culture, 25 July 1849.

[5] On the situation in Prussia, see 'Erörterungen der bisherigen Verhältnisse der Hebammen und Wickelfrauen zu Berlin', *Verhandlungen der Gesellschaft für Geburtshilfe*, 6 (1852), 39–55, especially pp. 40–3. On the absence of such battles in the rest of Germany, see Lindemann, 'Midwives in Braunschweig', p. 188, n. 3.

licensed by this board. Midwives were also admonished 'not to wait until the last hour' to call a physician during difficult cases; not to prescribe medicines without the knowledge, and presumably the approval, of a physician; and to act in a friendly fashion toward other midwives who might be called to the same case. Anyone who disobeyed these rules was threatened with 'serious punishment'.[6]

What is perhaps most striking to the modern reader is the vagueness of this edict. The midwife was to be examined, yet nothing was said either about how she was to learn midwifery or about the content of the examination. Indeed, the governing bodies seemed more concerned with controlling the behaviour of the midwife than with determining the extent of her knowledge.[7] Later ordinances would be more specific. A royal medical edict in 1725, for example, elaborated on the midwife's proper behaviour, exhorting her to remain sober day and night, and to report to the authorities any 'suspicious persons seeking indecent advice or help' (an obvious allusion to women seeking abortifacients). It also stated more forcefully the prohibition against any and all 'internal and external cures, both for married and single women, as well as pregnant and parturient women and children'.[8] But most importantly, this edict marked the beginning of the government's interest in the education of midwives, for it stipulated that they attend anatomical lectures in which cadavers would be used to instruct them on the nature and structure of the organs of parturition.

Such instruction was possible because Frederick William I (1713–40) had already created a series of educational institutions, all designed to improve the quality of medical care available to both his soldiers and the population at large. Concerned particularly with the great losses his army suffered every year because of sickness, the so-called Soldier King converted his father's Orangerie into a botanical garden, and he founded the *Theatrum anatomicum* for public dissections (1713), the *Collegium medico-chirurgicum* for instruction in anatomy, physics, botany, and chemistry (1723), and, immediately following the issuance of the new medical edict, the Charité hospital in Berlin for clinical training (1726).[9] Although the primary purpose of these institutions was to train an

[6] For a verbatim reprinting of the medical edict of 1685, including some analysis, see M. Stürzbecher, *Beiträge zur Berliner Medizingeschichte* (Berlin, 1966), pp. 1–43. Section 18 appears on p. 32. For other work on the edict of 1685, see R. Münch, *Gesundheitswesen im 18. und 19. Jahrhundert. Das Berliner Beispiel* (Berlin, 1995), pp. 27–33; J. Geyer-Kordesch, 'German Medical Education in the Eighteenth Century: The Prussian Context and its Influence', in W. F. Bynum and R. Porter (eds), *William Hunter and the Eighteenth-century Medical World* (Cambridge, 1985), 177–205. Brandenburg-Prussia was not the first government to regulate midwives. Several cities in southern Germany had passed midwifery ordinances in the fifteenth and sixteenth centuries. Moreover, in the Netherlands, the town of Delft started regulating midwives as early as 1656, and Amsterdam followed in 1668. See Wiesner, 'Midwives of South Germany', p. 83.

[7] This would be consistent with the argument of some scholars that the early modern State linked qualifications more to the person than to his or her work. See T. H. Broman, 'Rethinking Professionalization: Theory, Practice, and Professional Ideology in Eighteenth-century German Medicine', *Journal of Modern History*, 67 (1995), 835–72.

[8] Quotations are from the royal medical edict of 1725, cited in Stürzbecher, *Beiträge*, p. 93.

[9] P. Diepgen and E. Heischkel, *Die Medizin an der Berliner Charité bis zur Gründung der Universität* (Berlin, 1935); J. Geyer-Kordesch, 'German Medical Education'; Dr Schickert, *Die militärärztlichen Bildungsanstalten von ihrer Gründung bis zur Gegenwart* (Berlin, 1895); J. W. Dudenhausen,

advanced corps of army surgeons, both civilian students of medicine and surgery, and midwives, were encouraged to attend classes as well. Indeed, in order to advance knowledge of midwifery, the Charité began as early as 1727 to take in 'debauched women' (*liederliche Weibsstücke*) and place them in a separate room for the specific purpose of clinical instruction.[10]

We know little about the nature of the clinical training that took place in the Charité other than that midwives had a room near the obstetric ward so that they could be close at hand during deliveries. However, even if these women managed to receive some practical and theoretical training in the hospital, it appears that the majority of aspirants did not follow this route but, rather, acquired their knowledge either by apprenticing themselves to experienced midwives, studying with the local town or district doctor (*Physicus*), or, for those who could read, availing themselves of one of the growing number of catechisms for midwives.[11] By the mid-eighteenth century, however, this arrangement no longer satisfied Prussian authorities, such as Johann Peter Süßmilch, member of the high consistory and a well-known national economist. One of the leading proponents of cameralistic thinking in Prussia, Süßmilch advanced the idea that the key to a nation's strength lay in its ability to stimulate economic growth and to amass wealth within its borders. To achieve this goal, the nation required, most importantly, a large and healthy population. Süßmilch thus turned his attention not only to collecting information about the rates of birth, marriage, and death, but also to reducing morbidity and lowering mortality, especially infant mortality. It was within this context that he grew concerned with the quality of care midwives offered and began to promote the establishment of a school of midwifery at the Charité hospital.[12]

Süßmilch, together with the directors of the city police and of the Charité, developed a plan for a midwifery school modelled on a similar institute in Paris, something which surely made an impact on the Francophilic King. There, at the Hôtel Dieu, a lying-in ward had been founded as early as 1630 for the purpose of educating female midwives, who received a three-month course of instruction from the *maîtresse sage-femme* (master midwife). However, what might have impressed Süßmilch more was the Hôtel Dieu's decision in

M. Stürzbecher, and M. Engel (eds), *Die Hebamme im Spiegel der Hebammenlehrbuecher* (Berlin, 1985), p. 2; H.-P. Wolff and J. Wolff, 'Die Berliner Hebammen-Schule', *Wissenschaftliche Zeitschrift der Humboldt-Universität zu Berlin, Math.-Nat. R.*, 36 (1987), pp. 47–9. The *Collegium medico-chirurgicum*, created in 1723 as a medical college, is not to be confused with the *Collegium medicum*, which was the government health board created in 1685.

[10] Cited in G. L. Mamlock, 'Zur Geschichte des Charitékrankenhauses', *Charité-Annalen*, 29 (1905), 61–86, p. 70.

[11] Ibid.; F. L. Augustin, *Die Königliche Preußische Medicinalverfassung* (Potsdam, 1818), p. 524; Dudenhausen, Stürzbecher, and Engel (eds), *Die Hebamme*; J. Wilke (ed.), *Die königliche Residenz Berlin und die Mark Brandenburg im 18. Jahrhundert. Johann Peter Süßmilch. Schriften und Briefe* (Berlin, 1994), p. 279.

[12] See Wilke (ed.), *Die königliche Residenz Berlin*, 278–91; V. John, 'Johann Peter Süßmilch', in *Allgemeine deutsche Biographie*, 37 (1894), 188–95. Süßmilch was strongly influenced by such British political economists as William Petty. On the importance of cameralism in Süßmilch's thoughts, see Stürzbecher, *Beiträge*, p. 94.

1745 to set up classes in anatomy and obstetrics. Six years later, Prussia followed suit; the same year that Göttingen founded the first German university clinic for obstetrics. Moreover, shortly afterwards Stockholm established a school of midwifery, followed by Copenhagen, Kassel, Braunschweig, and Jena, to name just a few.[13]

Clearly, the decision to improve midwifery education was part of a broader programme, evident throughout Europe, of centralization and medicalization characteristic of the absolutist State. A growing desire to reduce mortality, combat disease, and in general to implement 'enlightened' principles of rule, led several national governments to institute various measures designed both to acquire more information about the nation's population (through the collection of birth, marriage, and death statistics) and to regulate the various healers responsible for the nation's health.[14]

Throughout Europe, therefore, the mid-eighteenth century marked a turning point in the education and licensing of midwives. From this point on, the story is one of ever-greater regulation, marked in part by the creation of formalized training programmes. Still, effective control did not occur overnight, and Prussia's decision to found a midwifery school in 1751 should not be exaggerated. The 'school' did not, for example, refer to a physical space for the education of midwives, but rather to a course of instruction that took them to different educational institutions around the city. Pupils attended lectures at the *Collegium medico-chirurgicum*. They observed practical demonstrations on cadavers in the anatomical theatre, and they visited the Charité for their clinical training. The lack of physical space was matched by the absence of a permanent faculty. Midwives usually received instruction from surgeons who lacked specific training in obstetrics, and who changed positions so frequently that it was nearly impossible to establish any consistency in the nature of the instruction being provided.[15]

Additional measures in the late eighteenth and early nineteenth centuries attempted to remedy these problems, a clear indication of the State's *gradual* move to control more and more aspects of midwifery. Thus, in 1779, an independent professorship in midwifery was established in Berlin. In 1791, any surgeon wishing to provide clinical training in midwifery had first to pass an examination in obstetrics himself, and, in 1802, the government published elaborate

[13] On Berlin's establishment of a school of midwifery in 1751, see Universitätsarchiv der Humboldt-Universität Berlin, Nr. 802, Royal Ministry of the Interior to the Minister of State, Eichhorn, 2 August 1846. On Paris, see J. Donnison, *Midwives and Medical Men. A History of Inter-Professional Rivalries and Women's Rights* (New York, 1977), pp. 18, 24, 27; H. Fassbender, *Geschichte der Geburtshilfe* (Hildesheim, 1964), pp. 142–6, 245. On the founding of the other institutes, see K. Sudhoff, 'Aus der Geschichte des Charité-Krankenhauses zu Berlin', *Muenchener medicinische Wochenschrift*, 57 (1910), 1015–18; Fassbender, *Geschichte der Geburtshilfe*, pp. 251–4. These sources attest to the influence Paris had not only in Prussia, but in other European lands as well.

[14] G. Rosen, 'Cameralism and the Concept of Medical Police', *Bulletin of the History of Medicine*, 27 (1953), 21–42. Filippini discusses the impact of such 'enlightened' thinking on Italian rulers in Filippini, 'The Church, the State and Childbirth', pp. 162–3.

[15] Augustin, *Die Königliche Preußische Medicinalverfassung*, pp. 524–5; Diepgen and Heischkel, *Die Medizin*, p. 145; Wolff and Wolff, 'Die Berliner Hebammen-Schule', p. 47.

instructions dictating exactly what material the professor of midwifery must cover in his classes.[16]

As a result of these and other measures, a rigorous training programme for midwives was finally in place by the early nineteenth century. Accordingly, each year 30 pupils from throughout the State attended classes at the Charité for a five-month period. To assert its control over the make-up of this group, the government dictated that anyone who wished to attend had to produce three documents: a legal certificate from her local magistrate stating that she would receive an official position as a midwife upon completing the course; a medical certificate from the district or municipal medical officer attesting that 'she possessed all the traits required of a midwife'; and a certificate from a preacher affirming that she had 'so far led an orderly and moral life'.[17] Whether there was competition for these positions among women who resided outside of Berlin is unclear. Leaving one's own family for an extended period of time would certainly have been a hardship for many women. On the other hand, since the local authorities paid for the instruction, and the graduates were guaranteed employment upon return to their home towns, the incentives were strong.[18] Certainly, in Berlin, competition was stiff, and some women applied three or four years in a row before finally gaining admission to the school.[19]

Once enrolled, the midwifery pupils underwent a highly standardized course of instruction, an indication of the government's attempt to ensure a high level of competence. The pupils attended lectures six days a week, for one hour a day, covering basic anatomy and physiology, normal pregnancies, births, and confinements, and irregular pregnancies and births. Complementing these theoretical lectures were practical lessons in childbirth. At each delivery the pupils attended, one was selected to manage the birth all the way through to the discarding of the placenta, three others assisted (which included giving a full examination to the mother), and as many came to observe as wished. The pupils also attended two one-hour classes a week, where they learned how to examine the parturient women. At the end of the five months of instruction, the pupils had to submit to an examination which, if they passed, ensured them a place in the State's medical hierarchy.[20]

[16] On the professorship for midwifery, see M. Lenz, *Geschichte der königlichen Friedrich-Wilhelms-Universität zu Berlin*, 5 vols, vol. 3 (Halle, 1910), pp. 90–2; O. Scheibe, 'Zweihundert Jahre des Charité-Krankenhauses zu Berlin', *Charité-Annalen*, 34 (1910), 1–178, esp. p. 85. The instructions from 1802 are published in Augustin, *Die Königliche Preußische Medicinalverfassung*, pp. 525–35.

[17] Augustin, *Die Königliche Preußische Medicinalverfassung*, p. 527.

[18] On the financial arrangements, see ibid., pp. 524–5.

[19] This was the experience of both Caroline Fredericke Zakrzewski, who was finally accepted to the school in 1839, and her daughter, Marie Elizabeth Zakrzewska, who began her studies ten years later. Martin Ludwig Zakrzewski discussed the problems his wife encountered in Geheimes Staatsarchiv, Preussisches Kulturministerium, Rep. 76I, Sekt. 31, Lit. Z, Nr. 2, Martin Zakrzewski to the State Minister, 13 July 1841. Marie Zakrzewska discussed her own problems in C. H. Dall (ed.), *A Practical Illustration of 'Woman's Right to Labour': Or, A Letter from Marie E. Zakrzewska, MD* (Boston, 1860), 58–60.

[20] Moreover, each year, the two pupils who were slated to practise in Berlin were selected for a more rigorous course of instruction. They acquired their skills and knowledge over a two-year period, which included two five-month sessions in the theory and practice of midwifery, and an

Thus, at a time when American midwives received no formal training, and American medical students graduated from medical school without ever having attended a single birth, midwifery pupils at the Charité usually managed four or five births over the course of their five months of instruction, they assisted in a few dozen more, and they observed as many as 100 deliveries.[21] In exchange for pursuing a rigorous course of instruction, they received certain protections under the law. They were licensed to attend normal births on their own and to assist physicians in case of complications. Both of these rights, however, came under question in the nineteenth century as physicians tried not only to redefine their own responsibilities to include normal births, but also to replace midwives with swaddling women when they needed assistants. In the subsequent battles, midwives found that their status as licensed practitioners protected them from both swaddling women and physicians, thus quelling competition from both 'below' and 'above'.

Swaddling Women

Swaddling women occupied an unusual niche among providers of health care. Although not licensed by the State, they were subject to regulation. In Berlin, they attended a three-month course of instruction at the university's obstetrics clinic, where they learned about the 'care and treatment of women in pregnancy, childbirth, and childbed, and of newborns'.[22] This instruction did not, however, authorize them to handle deliveries themselves. Rather, their duties and responsibilities were restricted solely to assisting physicians during delivery.

Throughout the first half of the century, the status of these women remained disputed. In 1825, the year Prussia established new medical regulations, the government dictated that the obstetrician's assistant *had* to be a midwife, not a swaddling woman. Although it lifted this restriction three years later, the role of swaddling women in the medical hierarchy, and particularly their relationship to midwives, remained contested. By the 1830s, several midwives were registering formal complaints with the city police. Their target was Wilhelm Busch, Professor of Obstetrics at the University of Berlin, whom they accused of ignoring government statutes. According to these statutes, either a licensed obstetrician or a licensed midwife had to accompany medical students who attended poor women in their homes during labour. However, Busch had been permitting, and even encouraging, his students to take along swaddling women since they

additional three-month session during the summer when they lived in the hospital and supervised most of the deliveries. See Universitätsarchiv der Humboldt-Universität Berlin, Nr. 802, Esse, 'Instruction für die, in der mit dem Königlichen Charité-Krankenhause verbundenen Hebammen-Lehranstalt auszubildenen Hebammenschülerinnen', 12 October 1846; Schmidt, 'Die geburtshülflich-klinischen Institute der Königlichen Charité', *Annalen des Charité-Krankenhauses*, 1 (1850), 485–523, esp. pp. 503–4.

[21] On the situation in America, see J. W. Leavitt, *Brought to Bed. Childbearing in America, 1750–1950* (New York, 1986).

[22] 'Erörterungen der bisherigen Verhältnisse der Hebammen und Wickelfrauen zu Berlin', *Verhandlungen der Gesellschaft für Geburtshilfe*, 6 (1852), 39–55, p. 39.

had less authority at the bedside. He saw this as a way of giving his students as much independence as possible. In their formal complaints, midwives requested that the government be more stringent in keeping students from working with swaddling women. But they also made clear their desire that Busch should stop training women for such work, and, indeed, that the position be abolished totally. Although the government was not yet ready to take such a radical step, it did, as a result of these complaints, keep a watchful eye on Busch, admonishing him constantly to comply with its instructions.[23]

However, things did not come to a head until the next decade, when physicians joined together in order to try and take control of the situation. The 1840s were, in general, a decade of radical medical reform, when physicians throughout Germany formed medical societies, promoting scientific research and collegiality within their own ranks. At the same time, they petitioned State governments to raise the qualifications necessary for practising medicine. Much has been written on physicians' battles to abolish the categories of 'surgeons of the first class' and 'surgeons of the second class', and to establish instead a single medical examination and a single licence for practice. What has received less attention were the proposed reforms concerning obstetrics. At the time, medical students did not need to qualify in obstetrics in order to be licensed as physicians. Indeed, the label 'obstetrician' (*Geburtshelfer*) applied to an entirely separate class of medical practitioners. These practitioners held an inferior position in the medical hierarchy, positioned just below surgeons of the second class and just above midwives, and grouped together with dentists and opticians.[24] In the 1840s, a group of physicians interested in obstetrical practice sought to alter this arrangement. The battle that eventually erupted over the proper place of midwives and swaddling women in the medical hierarchy can only be understood against this backdrop.

Contested Domains: Midwives, Obstetricians, and Swaddling Women

No one shaped the terms of the debate over medical reform in Prussia more than Joseph Hermann Schmidt (1804–52), associate professor of obstetrics at the University of Berlin, director of the midwifery institute at the Charité, and arguably the most powerful medical adviser in the Prussian government at the time. He had been brought to Berlin in 1844 as a member of the Ministry of Culture, with the explicit charge of helping to reform the State's system of medical education and

[23] The material on this debate is extensive, and can be found in Geheimes Staatsarchiv, Preussisches Kulturministerium, Rep. 76Va, Sekt. 2, Tit. X, Nr. 8, Bd. V, 135–256. See also Potsdam-Brandenburgisches Landeshauptarchiv, Rep. 30 Berlin, C-Polizei Präsidium, Tit. 50, Nr. 2232, Ministry of Culture to Midwives Freyer, Zakrzewski and Genossin, 14 January 1842; Geheimes Staatsarchiv, Preussisches Kulturministerium, Rep. 76VIIIA, Nr. 896, Letter from Carl Mayer, President of the Society for Obstetricians in Berlin, to the State Minister, 20 December 1847.

[24] Joseph Hermann Schmidt, *Die Reform der Medizinalverfassung Preußens* (Berlin, 1846), p. 15. On the meaning of the medical regulations of 1825, see C. Huerkamp, *Der Aufstieg der Ärzte im 19. Jahrhundert. Vom gelehrten Stand zum professionellen Experten. Das Beispiel Preußens* (Göttingen, 1985), pp. 45–50.

licensing. Schmidt was, in fact, responsible for drafting the plan that laid the foundation for the State's new medical regulations, which were finally instituted in 1852. At the time of his move to Berlin, he was also author of the prize-winning, government-sanctioned, *Textbook of Midwifery*, which remained the State's standard text on this subject through the 1850s.[25]

Schmidt advocated a middle ground when it came to defining the midwife's place in the medical hierarchy. As the government correctly pointed out, his textbook sought to improve the midwives' level of knowledge by teaching them the theory and practice of midwifery at the same time that it introduced them to the laws regulating their practice. It instructed them, for example, that their domain extended over normal births alone; for abnormal births they were required to send for an obstetrician. And Schmidt did not hesitate to impress upon midwives how they were to act once the obstetrician arrived:

> The midwife is to provide an answer for all questions asked of her ... [She is to] follow exactly what he says, even if it deviates from the usual instructions of her textbook and from the lectures of her teacher, because the limited knowledge of the midwife makes it impossible to judge why a deviation might be necessary in this case. The obstetrician also has no obligation at all to justify his procedures to the midwife. However, for the latter, it is the most sacred duty to comply with [the obstetrician's] superior insights without objection.[26]

These are hardly the words of someone fighting to place female midwives on an equal footing with obstetricians. But that was also never Schmidt's goal. On the contrary, he believed quite firmly that the midwife's position was subordinate to that of the obstetrician. Indeed, had he not taken this position, it is difficult to imagine his textbook having won the approval of the government, especially since several prestigious professors of obstetrics had sat on the prize committee. Still, this did not prevent Schmidt from believing that the rights and responsibilities of the midwife had to be protected. These rested upon a division of duties such that 'the obstetrician is assigned chiefly to the irregular (unusual) cases, the midwives, on the other hand, chiefly to the regular (usual) cases'.[27] This, however, was exactly the arrangement that a group of Berlin obstetricians set out to challenge in the 1840s.

In February 1844, a small group of practising obstetricians came together to form a scientific society dedicated to their specialty. Carl Mayer, a Prussian health officer and renowned obstetrician, provided the inspiration for the Berlin Society of Obstetrics and was duly elected its first president. At first, Schmidt had also supported this organization and was rewarded with the vice-presidency, thus providing the Society with a link to the government. This

[25] Biographical information on Schmidt can be found in P. Fraatz, *Der Paderborner Kreisarzt Joseph Hermann Schmidt (Abhandlungen zur Geschichte der Medizin und der Naturwissenschaften*, vol. 29) (Berlin, 1939).

[26] J. H. Schmidt, *Lehrbuch der Geburtskunde fuer die Hebammen in der Koeniglichen Preussischen Staaten*, 2nd edn (Berlin, 1850), p. 186.

[27] Ibid., p. 1.

apparently paid off, for by November the Society had received a formal endorsement from the Ministry of Culture.[28]

This small group of physicians had come together, they explained, in order to raise standards in their field by promoting the 'art and science' of obstetrics. Their greatest complaint was that 'only a few physicians dedicate themselves to [obstetrics] with full love, with a scientific sense, and with the necessary skill, while, on the other hand, the number of those is very large who are often rough and unskilled enough and practise obstetrics as though it were a trade'.[29] The comment about tradesmen makes perfect sense, given that the official classification of Prussian health-care practitioners grouped obstetricians together with dentists and opticians. Their hope was to work with the State to abolish those health-care practitioners whose standards and style of practice lowered, in their eyes, the standing of the profession as a whole. This was certainly part of the agenda of Berlin's Society of Obstetrics, but as it turns out, they sought not only to distance themselves from the 'tradesmen' within their ranks, but also to claim some of the territory traditionally reserved for female midwives. For Schmidt, however, this was going too far, and a fierce battle broke out between Schmidt and most of the Society's membership. Unfortunately for the latter, Schmidt had the government on his side.

Schmidt, who eventually resigned in protest over his colleagues' position on swaddling women, drafted a decree on the subject in September of 1847, which he sent to the government for feedback and ultimately for approval. He viewed as troublesome the growing number of swaddling women who delivered babies on their own, and used harsh words to describe the part obstetricians played in generating this state of affairs. Greed, he claimed, drove obstetricians to infringe upon the midwives' rights to normal, easy births. To make matters worse, an obstetrician rarely stayed at the bedside of the parturient woman, but, rather, returned to his other patients, leaving a swaddling woman with instructions to call him as soon as problems arose or the birth was about to occur. All too often, however, the swaddling woman ended up delivering the child herself, claiming either that the birth came on suddenly or that the obstetrician could not be found. 'In this way', Schmidt wrote with seeming annoyance, 'many disgraceful means are used on the part of obstetricians to extend their practice, on the one hand, and, on the other, to do so with the least possible inconvenience to themselves by chiefly using swaddling women to carry on their practice'.[30] Schmidt's suggestion was either to forbid physicians' use of swaddling women outright, or to keep the public informed of the limited skills of the swaddling women, to warn the swaddling women more forcefully of the punishments that awaited them if they overstepped their boundaries, and to establish birth certificates, analogous to death certificates, that would require a physician or a

[28] 'Einleitung', *Verhandlungen der Gesellschaft für Geburtshülfe in Berlin*, 1 (1846), 6–14.
[29] Ibid., p. 6.
[30] The decree is published verbatim in 'Erörterungen der bisherigen Verhältnisse', 42–4, p. 42.

midwife to swear under oath whether they had performed the delivery themselves.[31]

Upon receiving the draft of this proposal, the government requested responses from both the Berlin Society of Obstetricians and from Professor Busch, who, although a member of the Society, shouldered a particular responsibility as the one who trained swaddling women in his clinic. Together these two documents presented a series of arguments for the necessity, even the urgency, of retaining swaddling women as medical assistants. Busch's report, which was far less detailed, focused primarily on the need for a large number of trained assistants, given the recent trend toward physician-attended births. In his estimation, the number of licensed midwives was inadequate to meet this demand.[32] The Society's report, submitted in December and penned by Mayer, took a more radical position, casting doubts on the advisability of retaining midwives as health care practitioners at all. At a time when physicians throughout Germany were struggling to improve their status, knowledge, and power by presenting medicine as more of a science than an art, Mayer's assertion carried particular meaning that a midwife 'is incapable of achieving deeper insight into the physiology of birth'.[33] This was especially meaningful since the rallying cry heard throughout the 1840s for 'scientific medicine' meant, for the majority of physicians, medicine based upon physiological principles.[34] The critical word in Mayer's sentence was 'incapable'. He was convinced that 'men alone possess the scientific acuity and impartiality of the ... senses', and that they alone have been responsible for raising obstetrics to its current state as a medical science. What particularly troubled Mayer was that 'the material, which is entrusted to women, is almost without exception lost to science'.[35] To remedy the situation, he argued forcefully for expanding the obstetrician's official responsibilities to include normal as well as abnormal births.

But what of the traditional objections raised against men entering the birthing room at any other time than during an emergency? Mayer addressed them one by one, dismissing each in turn. 'Does one believe', he asked, 'that the *modesty* of the parturient woman is harmed through the assistance of a man? Well, then, that is something the public must decide'. In response to the accusation that obstetricians intervened too readily, he responded that one need only read the Society's journal to know that their guiding principle is 'to let nature take its course', at least to the extent that it is possible. It may be, he confessed, that some practitioners use forceps too often, but one should not condemn the many because of the few. Rather, this should be seen as evidence that the educational level of a large number of obstetricians is still too low, and that the state should respond not by

[31] Ibid., p. 43.

[32] Geheimes Staatsarchiv, Preussisches Kulturministerium, Rep. 76 VIIIA, Nr. 896, Busch to Eichhorn, 24 September 1847.

[33] Geheimes Staatsarchiv, Preussisches Kulturministerium, Rep. 76 VIIIA, Nr. 896, Mayer to Eichhorn, 20 December 1847. Most likely Busch helped draft the Society's official report. See 'Erörterungen der bisherigen Verhältnisse', p. 50.

[34] A. M. Tuchman, *Science, Medicine, and the State. The Case of Baden, 1815–1871* (Oxford, 1993).

[35] Mayer to Eichhorn, 20 December 1847, p. 4.

keeping obstetricians out of the birthing room, but by promoting more attention to this subject in the universities.[36]

Having put forth his case for the superiority of the obstetrician over the midwife, Mayer then turned to the question of who should function as the physician's assistant. That obstetricians required assistants was clear to him. It stemmed from the fact that they could not remain at the labouring mother's side throughout the entire birthing process. Nor, Mayer argued, was it necessary for them to do so. A properly trained assistant would know when to call the physician away from his other visits, and she would be able to take care of the mother and child after the delivery had been completed. Mayer was very clear about who should *not* be the obstetrician's assistant. In perhaps the most emphatic section of the report, he declared: '*If, then, for the benefit of the parturient women and for the good of obstetrics overall, obstetricians are to retain their recently won terrain, then it is absolutely necessary that they be freed from the constraint that they take a midwife with them to deliveries.*'[37]

Language that promoted the lifting of 'constraints' in the name of 'freedom' was common fare in the months just prior to the outbreak of the revolutions of 1848. Yet one need not turn too many more pages in Mayer's report to recognize that the Berlin Society's concern was more about establishing its own power over midwives than in creating a system free of coercion. Midwives make poor assistants, Mayer explained, because as soon as they begin practising, they act as though they 'know anything and everything better than all obstetricians and physicians'.[38] As a result, they often refuse to call a physician or, if they do, they fail to follow his instructions. Thinking perhaps about the constant accusations waged by the Berlin midwives, Mayer also complained bitterly that they openly denounced physicians to the public at large. In other words, as Mayer clearly stated, 'the great advantage of these [swaddling] women over midwives is that they have no rights of their own, that they are indeed only servants [*dienende Personen*] in whose natural interests it lies to earn the satisfaction of their superiors through conscientious obedience'.[39] In short, as he concluded a few pages later, 'the direction of the delivery is not a two-way, but a one-way street. The obstetrician gives the order and supervises, the swaddling woman obeys and carries out [the orders]'.[40]

Mayer was not misrepresenting the situation. Prussian midwives not only had rights, but they had been fighting to protect them since the 1830s. They continued to keep a watchful eye on Busch, and submitted lists to the police, detailing the times that swaddling women had accompanied medical students to the homes of the city poor. Small wonder, then, that Mayer, Busch, and the 26 other obstetricians who signed this report felt so passionately about the issue of swaddling women. Midwives were not servile creatures, willing to accept the obstetrician's word at face value, and to watch quietly as male physicians crossed traditional

[36] Ibid., pp. 8–11.
[37] Ibid., p. 12 (Mayer's emphasis). See also pp. 31–4.
[38] Ibid., p. 18.
[39] Ibid., p. 22.
[40] Ibid., p. 24.

boundaries and claimed as their own the rights and responsibilities promised to the midwives by law. The repeated admonitions Busch received from the government suggest that the midwives' complaints carried some weight. They had, moreover, a formidable friend in Schmidt.

In January, one month after the Ministry of Culture received the Berlin Society's report, Schmidt staked out his position again, castigating his colleagues for blurring the line between midwives and swaddling women. With an argument that parallelled Mayer's use of science to distinguish between obstetricians and midwives, Schmidt explained that midwives were taught 'small science' (*kleine Wissenschaft*), which helped them to recognize the boundary between natural and artificial assistance. 'One calls this small science with its particular rules', he emphasized, '"*the art of midwifery*"; the state does not yet recognize "*the art of swaddling*"'.[41] Schmidt claimed he had no objection to the use of swaddling women as assistants. What he wished to stop was the practice whereby obstetricians used swaddling women as proxies during childbirth. In that case, he reasoned, they were basically doing the work of the midwife, and should, therefore, be trained as midwives. That, however, meant training in the official midwifery schools of the State, not in the university clinic or in the private practice of an individual physician. The fundamental point, then, for a man like Schmidt who believed so firmly in State control, was that the position of swaddling woman should either be abolished or officially recognized, in which case the women should be examined and licensed like all other medical personnel.

Schmidt may have hoped for speedy action, but political events prevented the government from reaching consensus. Less than six weeks after Schmidt submitted his opinion to the government, revolution broke out in the streets of Berlin. During the period of greatest turmoil—between the outbreak of revolution in the spring of 1848, its evident failure in the summer of 1849, and the onset of the reaction in the winter of 1850—the government went through a series of rapid changes that resulted as well in a succession of alternative proposals for resolving the problem of swaddling women. In July 1849, for example, when the royal government had firmly re-established itself in Berlin, but the period of extreme reaction had not yet set in, the police sent a report to the Ministry of Culture that fell short of recommending that the position be outlawed. Although it sided unequivocally with Schmidt on this issue, it preferred to reason with obstetricians, agreeing that the midwife may have been problematic in the past because she had been poorly instructed, but assuring them that the new *Textbook* (a new edition of Schmidt's textbook that had just come out) explained quite clearly that she was to be 'the true assistant to the obstetrician'. This was related, of course, to the question, raised by both Schmidt and the Society of Obstetrics, as to who should have primary responsibility for normal births. Here again, however, the police chose not to intervene, preferring instead to 'leave it to the free arrangement between the public and obstetricians as to how far the latter can absorb

[41] Geheimes Staatsarchiv, Preussisches Kulturministerium, Rep. 76VIIIA, Nr. 896, Schmidt to Lehnert, 16 January 1848, p. 9.

the practice of midwifery to which they also have a right'.[42] Where the police had, however, little patience with obstetricians was in their use of proxies. Interestingly, only midwives were required by law to remain at the bedside of the mother-to-be; obstetricians had free reign to come and go. Still, the police felt quite strongly that the entire problem would be resolved if obstetricians would forgo this freedom and fulfil their duty to remain with the parturient woman until she delivered her child safely, and mother and child were well taken care of.

The government's inclination, in 1849, to rely on education, persuasion, and the public's right to choose did not last long. A move toward ever-greater legislation of medical affairs, which had been growing throughout the 1840s, resulted, in February 1852, in an official government decree severely restricting the activities of swaddling women. 'From now on', it began, 'in order to curb the mischief caused by swaddling women, the police [*Polizei-Präsidium*], as the supervisory authority, will punish those obstetricians who send a swaddling woman in their place instead of appearing themselves at the delivery, or who, when they leave the parturient woman, entrust her to a swaddling woman.'[43]

In evaluating the significance of this legislation, one must begin by acknowledging that the Berlin Society had lost its battle for swaddling women, a clear sign that elite physicians had not yet formed a powerful enough lobby to ensure that State officials would support them in their quest to replace other health care providers. Yet, in other ways, obstetricians had won. That same year, the Prussian government totally revamped its medical system, ending the tri-partite division into physician, surgeons of the first class, and surgeons of the second class, and dictating that anyone wishing to practise medicine in the State had to demonstrate mastery in medicine, surgery, and obstetrics.[44] As a result, obstetricians, who had previously 'been cut off from . . . physicians, and placed together with opticians and dentists', were now included among the medical elite.

And what of midwives? The restrictions placed on the use of swaddling women in 1852 gave greater legal backing to the government's assertion that midwives were the 'true assistants to obstetricians'. But the statement was, of course, highly ambiguous. The midwife was being told that she was both the true *assistant* and the *true* assistant. She was, in other words, both a loser and a winner in this game. On the one hand, she was reminded of her subordinate position, integrated into a medical hierarchy that now placed obstetrics in the hands of a medical elite. Yet at the same time, midwives had won their battle to secure their place in this hierarchy, successfully challenging efforts on the part of both swaddling women and physicians to eliminate them entirely. She may have been subjected to greater state control, but 50 years following this legislation, at a time when midwives in the United States were struggling for their survival, Prussian midwives still attended over 90 per cent of all births.[45] Perhaps, in the end, it may be

[42] Geheimes Staatsarchiv, Preussisches Kulturministerium, Rep. 76 VIIIA, Nr. 882, Police Headquarters to the Ministry of Culture, 25 July 1849.

[43] 'Erörterungen der bisherigen Verhältnisse', pp. 53–4.

[44] Schmidt, *Die Reform der Medizinalverfassung*, p. 16. See also Huerkamp, *Der Aufstieg*, pp. 50–9.

[45] Huerkamp, *Der Aufstieg*, p. 157.

more appropriate to cast them as victors, but it was a victory for which they had paid a price.

Acknowledgements

I wish to thank Charlotte G. Borst, Susan L. Smith, and two anonymous referees for their extremely helpful comments on an earlier version of this article. Research for this article was funded by a grant from the German Academic Exchange Service (DAAD).

Social History of Medicine Vol. 18 No. 1 © *The Society for the Social History of Medicine 2005, all rights reserved.*
doi:10.1093/sochis/hki003

Sanitary Policing and the Local State, 1873–1874: A Statistical Study of English and Welsh Towns

By CHRISTOPHER HAMLIN★

SUMMARY. This article examines local sanitary policing in extra-metropolitan English and Welsh towns and cities in the period 1873–4. It combines two parliamentary returns, one focusing on the appointments by towns of sanitary officers (inspectors of nuisances and medical officers), the other listing the number of nuisance cases and modes of resolution. The article uses these databases to examine the identification of nuisances in terms of region, town type, mode of government, population, and salary of the inspector. It considers also the effects of tenure and job security on nuisances identification, the effects of town wealth, and differences in the resolution of nuisance allegations by town type and region. The article shows a remarkable and perhaps unexpected sanitary activism, but also a considerable variability by region, town size, and town type.

KEYWORDS: England, Wales, urban sanitation, nuisances, public health, local government.

Most attention to the transformation of the nineteenth-century urban environment—particularly with respect to health—has focused on infrastructure development—namely, the building of sewers and waterworks, but also housing, gas, electricity, and transport. We know much less about the day-to-day policing of the environment: the registering of conditions deemed unacceptable—nuisances—and the instituting of legal processes leading to their elimination.

The policemen in question were the inspectors of nuisances. They were mandated by the Public Health Act of 1848 for the towns which adopted that act, and by the Public Health Act of 1872 for all urban (and rural) sanitary authorities. They were to do routinely a task that, during epidemic crises, had been done by doctors: that of scouring the town for whatever might endanger health, and instituting legal proceedings to have it removed or remedied. By the end of the century such inspectors, by then known as sanitary inspectors, commonly served as foot soldiers under the direction of medical officers of health, and their activities have generally been lost sight of in the now broadened domain of local public health administration.[1] But in the period under study here, medical officers, although also mandated by the 1872 Act, were still few, and often little involved in day-to-day public administration.[2]

The nuisances inspectors, by contrast, were on the front lines, and in many cases, were quite busy. A better understanding of the policing of nuisances during this period is important in four contexts.

The first is public health itself, both conceived in demographic terms as the decline in mortality and in administrative terms as the expansion of government

★Department of History, University of Notre Dame, 219 O'Shaughnessy Hall, Notre Dame, Indiana 46556–0368, USA. E-mail: hamlin.1@nd.edu

[1] A. Wohl, *Endangered Lives: Public Health in Victorian Britain* (Cambridge MA, 1983), pp. 193–5.
[2] Wohl, *Endangered Lives*, pp. 181–2.

to take responsibility for environmental quality with regard to health. Beginning with the passage of the first Nuisances Removal and Diseases Prevention Act of 1846 as an emergency measure against the coming of cholera, the corpus of Victorian nuisances legislation was driven by concern about acute epidemic disease. A good deal of what we know of the activities of nuisances inspection can be understood straightforwardly as efforts to rid towns of materials (particularly wastes and other decaying organic matters) and conditions (overcrowded or unfit dwellings), which were, by almost anyone's disease theory, implicated in some way in injury to health.[3] In this context, such policing will be of particular interest with regard to the response of local authorities to central government public health initiatives. It has been customary to see nineteenth-century towns as unenthusiastic participants in the revolution of government, succumbing grudgingly to rationality, professionalism, and accountability: 'Complaints about the apathy or open hostility of the local administrations employing them [medical officers] run like a *leitmotif* through the literature of nineteenth-century public health', Wohl rightly notes.[4] While the data reviewed below are subject to a variety of interpretations, they do reveal a magnitude of activity not easily consistent with such a view.

The second context is the relation of the rights of property to communal good. In seminal articles, Gerry Kearns highlighted both the enormity of the nineteenth-century assault on traditional property rights and its remarkable success—due in part to the cleverness of bureaucrats such as Edwin Chadwick in representing those impositions as protections of rights.[5] Neither the corpus of nuisances by-laws that began to appear in eighteenth-century local legislation nor the permissive and later mandatory legislation of mid-nineteenth-century public health acts marked the beginnings of the enforcement of public good over private rights in towns. And yet, Kearns is clearly right in seeing something qualitatively different in the magnitude of the new assault, and in the attempt to objectify those rights and goods, to regularize the policing, and, in some respects, to expand the domain of public goods. How, one may wonder, did the nuisance

[3] On implications of disease theories, see M. Pelling, *Cholera, Fever, and English Medicine, 1825–65* (Oxford, 1978); J. M. Eyler, *Victorian Social Medicine: The Ideas and Methods of William Farr* (Baltimore, 1979); C. Hamlin, 'Predisposing Causes and Public Health in the Early Nineteenth-Century Public Health Movement', *Social History of Medicine*, 5 (1992), 43–70; idem, *Public Health and Social Justice in the Age of Chadwick: Britain 1800–54* (Cambridge, 1998); P. Baldwin, *Contagion and the State in Europe, 1830–1930* (New York, 1999).

[4] Wohl, *Endangered Lives*, pp. 187–91; E. P. Hennock, 'Central/Local Government Relations in England, an Outline', *Urban History Yearbook* (1982), 38–47; H. Williams, 'Public Health and Local History', *Local Historian*, 14 (1980), 202–10; C. Hamlin, 'Muddling in Bumbledom: Local Governments and Large Sanitary Improvements: The Cases of Four British Towns, 1855–85', *Victorian Studies*, 32 (1988), 55–83; J. Prest, *Liberty and Locality: Parliament, Permissive Legislation, and Ratepayers' Democracies in the Nineteenth Century* (Oxford, 1990); P. J. Waller, *Town, City, and Nation in England, 1850–1914* (Oxford, 1983), p. 283; G. Kearns, 'Town Hall and Whitehall: Sanitary Intelligence in Liverpool, 1840–63', in S. Sheard and H. Power (eds), *Body and City: Histories of Urban Public Health* (Aldershot, 2000), 89–108.

[5] G. P. Kearns, 'Aspects of Cholera, Society, and Space in Nineteenth-Century England and Wales' (unpublished Ph.D. thesis, University of Cambridge, 1985) pp. 250–71; idem, 'Cholera, Nuisances, and Environmental Management in Islington, 1830–55', in W. F. Bynum and R. Porter (eds), *Living and Dying in London* (London, 1991), 94–125; idem, 'Private Property and Public Health Reform in England, 1830–70', *Social Science and Medicine*, 26 (1988), 187–99.

inspectors, who were to impose those constraints on rights, manage to do so? Could these unskilled municipal servants, lacking any security of tenure, really have acted effectively against the property-owners who made up the very local authorities which employed them?

Thirdly, and closely related, is the emergence of the common standards of urban amenity which it would be the task of local government to enforce. The range and variety of mid-nineteenth-century aetiology made it plausible to find conditions harmful to health almost anywhere one chose to look. Nuisances inspectors constantly faced decisions about what standards to enforce and in what degrees. Can dogs foul pavements or not? Why can I not keep pigs behind (or in) my dwelling? Following the suggestions of Norbert Elias, Mary Douglas, Bill Luckin, and others, one might explore how visible manners—including the ways one keeps up one's dwelling and surroundings—become a badge of middle-class membership.[6] Perhaps the concept of nuisance, drawing on the imperative of dirt as a general danger to health, figures centrally in the promulgation of middle-class standards of cleanliness as a very direct means of enforcing what are coming to be seen as obvious standards of decency. Lending credence to the importance of such cultural processes is the fact that in the data to be reviewed below of nuisances in over 500 extra-metropolitan English and Welsh towns, the vast majority of nuisance allegations are not contested. One may hypothesize that they were resolved so readily because those responsible were more embarrassed at being labelled dirty or indecent than outraged at the local state's violation of their presumed rights of property.[7]

The fourth context is the role of nuisances inspection in the development of the bureaucratic Weberian state. To romantic constitutionalists like Joshua Toulmin Smith, one of the most graphic horrors of the nineteenth century was the loss of traditional, and supposedly communal, modes of adjudicating conflict over the uses of public space and its replacement by the dictatorship of the so-called expert—here, the supposed science-based authority of the medical officer of health and his minion, the inspector of nuisances.[8] One need not indulge in Smith's romanticizing of the parish as the fount of democracy or his adoration of common law and constitution to recognize the abruptness of the shift in the mid-nineteenth century from nuisance as an accusation within a community of

[6] The classic primary source for such middle-class anxiety is G. and W. Grossmith, *The Diary of a Nobody*, edited by K. Flint (Oxford,1998). See also N. Elias, *The Civilizing Process. Sociogenetic and Psychogenetic Investigations*, edited by E. Dunning, J. Goudsblom, and S. Mennell (Oxford, 2000); M. Douglas, 'Environments at Risk', in B. Barnes and D. Edge (eds), *Science in Context* (Cambridge, MA, 1982), 260–75; idem, *Purity and Danger: An Analysis of the Concepts of Pollution and Taboo* (London, 1966); B. Luckin, *Questions of Power: Electricity and Environment in Inter-war Britain* (Manchester, 1990).

[7] C. Hamlin, 'Public Sphere to Public Health: The Transformation of "Nuisance"', in S. Sturdy (ed.), *Medicine, Health, and the Public Sphere in Britain, 1600–2000* (London, 2002), 189–204.

[8] J. T. Smith, *Practical Proceedings for the Removal of Nuisances to Health and Safety: And for the Execution of Sewerage Works, in Towns and in Rural Parishes, under the Common Law and Under Recent Statutes*, 4th edn (London, 1867). See Waller, *Town, City, and Nation in England*, ch. 6; H. Finer, *English Local Government* (London, 1933), p. 233. Finer argued that the work of such unsung local experts was a key factor in achieving 'the standard of living and social well-being of the world today'.

presumed equals to nuisance as a summary declaration by a designated professional nuisance-knower (who, however, for most of the century, could hardly be said to possess the training or credentials that accredited one as a scientific authority. While there were voluntary certification programmes by the mid-1880s the first generation of nuisance inspectors were to be accepted as authoritative without having any of the usual accoutrements of authority.[9])

By no means will the data reviewed below answer the questions posed above. More finely grained local studies must do much of that work. Yet it has been hard to address the questions on even a local basis because nationwide analyses of local government activity have been relatively few. These data and analyses do offer a snapshot of sanitary regulation across the nation as a whole. They allow us to test, albeit tentatively, some hypotheses. They also provide us with a baseline against which to compare earlier and later regulation both within particular places and across regions or types of towns.

The databases that form the empirical basis of this article were constructed in the early 1870s and reflect about a quarter of a century of evolution in nuisances legislation. The emergency Nuisances Removal and Diseases Prevention Act passed in 1846, was renewed in 1847, became permanent in 1848, was amended in 1855 and 1860, and finally incorporated into the general public health legislation in 1872 and 1875. The early nuisances removal acts, unlike the Public Health Act of 1848, need not be adopted by a town. All designated local authorities acquired a legal means for removing nuisances, understood initially as faulty drains, faulty or overcrowded dwellings, and accumulations of filth.[10] Much of the concern in 1855, the first occasion for serious parliamentary consideration of the implications of this legislation, dealt with noxious trades. Initially the designation of nuisances was left primarily to (two) medical men and confirmed by a Justice of the Peace. Any two properly qualified medical men could make such a designation.

With regard to public health nuisances, the composite legislation of the early 1870s marks the convergence of another legislative tradition—the appointment of a public inspector of nuisances. The inclusion of such a role in the job description of some municipal officer was not novel. Many local police acts of the eighteenth century conceived such a role primarily with regard to the continued functioning of public thoroughfares—a matter of dealing with occasional obstructions, drainage, the removal of garbage and other forms of household wastes, and structural trespass.[11] The Towns Improvement Clauses Act of 1847 included

[9] M. Laffin, *Local Government Officers: Professionalism, Power, and Accountability* (SSRC/Urban History/Politics Seminar, LSE, 1980); Wohl, *Endangered Lives*, p. 194; Finer, *English Local Government*, pp. 255–9.

[10] The 1855 Act was celebrated by Toulmin Smith, the great and controversial champion of common law, as embodying the principles of common law in requiring all local authorities to enforce environmental standards of health and safety (Smith, *Practical Proceedings for the Removal of Nuisances*, pp. 3, 22–5, 96–8). Yet he doubted it gave them any powers which they did not already hold under common law.

[11] F. H. Spencer, *Municipal Origins: An Account of English Private Bill Legislation Relating to Local Government, 1740–1835; With a Chapter on Private Bill Procedure* (London, 1911).

clauses dealing with the appointment of a specialist inspector of nuisances, which towns might use in local acts. The Public Health Act of 1848 drew on these and mandated the appointment of an inspector of nuisances by those towns in which local boards of health were established. Following the establishment of the Local Government Board (the LGB) in 1871, the Public Health Act of 1872 brought a degree of uniformity in designating extra-metropolitan units of local government as urban or rural sanitary authorities. These were the designated 'nuisance authorities'. They were to enforce the nuisances clauses in the various acts and instructed to appoint ('from time to time') a 'fit and proper person' as an inspector of nuisances.[12]

The newly-established LGB, drawing on precedent, also had something to say about what nuisances were and what this officer was to do. The new nuisances legislation effected an extraordinary narrowing of the concept. Traditionally, 'nuisance' had overlapped only occasionally with public health. For authors such as Blackstone and Burns, writing respectively on the common law and on parish administration, rowdiness and the regulation of a common scold were central. Matters of wastes disposal figured mainly with regard to pig-keeping.[13] The new nuisances legislation did not supersede common law, but, as Toulmin Smith complained, it did reorient attention toward space and health: accumulations of filth (of an unspecified nature), bad drains, unconsumed smoke, unsound or overcrowded dwellings, insufficient privies or water closets, uncleanly workplaces, and unhealthy dwellings. In November 1872, the newly-established LGB issued a job description for those inspectors of nuisances that it partially subsidized.[14] While very few of those considered here were subsidized, the job description, adapted from the Towns Clauses Act of 1847, probably outlines what most did. The inspector had responsibility for the new statutory nuisances, but also for some other forms of inspection. He was to keep an eye on the water supply, although not at the level of chemical analysis. He was to notify the medical officer of cases of contagious or epidemic disease, and to examine foodstuffs on sale for safety and adulteration.[15] The inspector was to follow a regimen of regular inspection of all portions of his district, to respond to citizen complaints, and to the instructions of the medical officer. He was to keep two books: a daily record of his inspections and findings, and a record, organized by place, of his inspections of each particular dwelling or site of commerce or manufacture.[16] We get a good sense of the routine of nuisances inspection by looking at the

[12] W. Glen and A. Glen, *The Law of Public Health* (London, 1875), p. 176. See S 189 of the 1875 Act.

[13] Hamlin, 'Public Sphere to Public Health', examines this transition.

[14] The LGB offered to pay 50 per cent of the salary of local officers appointed under its approval, but the policy was not popular (Wohl, *Endangered Lives*, pp. 191–2). For the origins of the policy see R. Lambert, *Sir John Simon, 1816–1904 and English Sanitary Administration* (London, 1965), p. 515.

[15] Glen and Glen, *The Law of Public Health*, pp. 611–15. Of these extra duties, it is unlikely that food adulteration or contagious disease cases figure much in the quantitative reports of nuisances. The former would be passed on to a public analyst, who would report separately. The latter would figure in the reports of medical officers of health.

[16] Two would probably be a minimum. The Shoreditch inspector was in fact keeping fifteen books in 1869, but some of these dealt with special aspects of metropolitan legislation. See H. Sutton, *St*

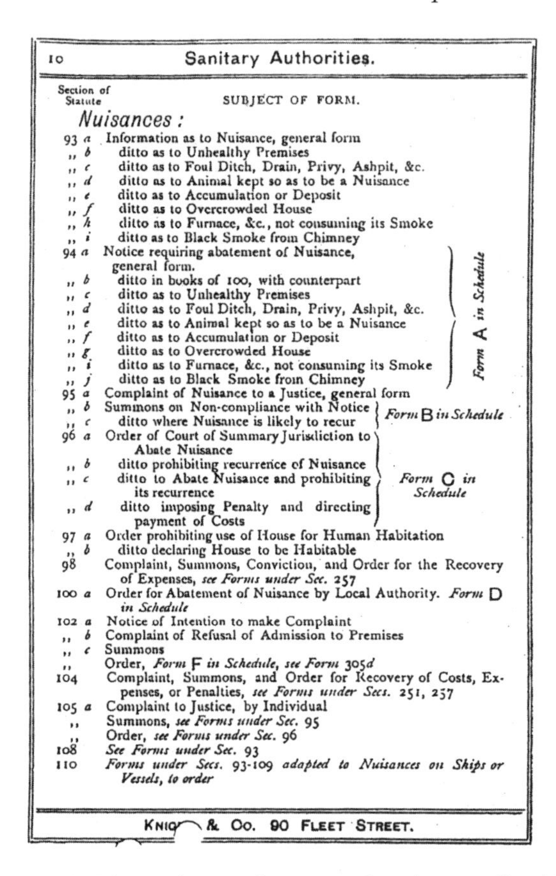

10 **Sanitary Authorities.**

Section of Statute	SUBJECT OF FORM.
	Nuisances:
93 *a*	Information as to Nuisance, general form
,, *b*	ditto as to Unhealthy Premises
,, *c*	ditto as to Foul Ditch, Drain, Privy, Ashpit, &c.
,, *d*	ditto as to Animal kept so as to be a Nuisance
,, *e*	ditto as to Accumulation or Deposit
,, *f*	ditto as to Overcrowded House
,, *h*	ditto as to Furnace, &c., not consuming its Smoke
,, *i*	ditto as to Black Smoke from Chimney
94 *a*	Notice requiring abatement of Nuisance, general form.
,, *b*	ditto in books of 100, with counterpart
,, *c*	ditto as to Unhealthy Premises
,, *d*	ditto as to Foul Ditch, Drain, Privy, Ashpit, &c.
,, *e*	ditto as to Animal kept so as to be a Nuisance
,, *f*	ditto as to Accumulation or Deposit
,, *g*	ditto as to Overcrowded House
,, *i*	ditto as to Furnace, &c., not consuming its Smoke
,, *j*	ditto as to Black Smoke from Chimney
	(94 *a*–*j*: *Form* A *in Schedule*)
95 *a*	Complaint of Nuisance to a Justice, general form
,, *b*	Summons on Non-compliance with Notice
,, *c*	ditto where Nuisance is likely to recur
	(95 *b*–*c*: *Form* B *in Schedule*)
96 *a*	Order of Court of Summary Jurisdiction to Abate Nuisance
,, *b*	ditto prohibiting recurrence of Nuisance
,, *c*	ditto to Abate Nuisance and prohibiting its recurrence
,, *d*	ditto imposing Penalty and directing payment of Costs
	(96 *a*–*d*: *Form* C *in Schedule*)
97 *a*	Order prohibiting use of House for Human Habitation
,, *b*	ditto declaring House to be Habitable
98	Complaint, Summons, Conviction, and Order for the Recovery of Expenses, *see Forms under Sec.* 257
100 *a*	Order for Abatement of Nuisance by Local Authority. *Form* D *in Schedule*
102 *a*	Notice of Intention to make Complaint
,, *b*	Complaint of Refusal of Admission to Premises
,, *c*	Summons
,,	Order, *Form* F *in Schedule, see Form* 305*d*
104	Complaint, Summons, and Order for Recovery of Costs, Expenses, or Penalties, *see Forms under Secs.* 251, 257
105 *a*	Complaint to Justice, by Individual
,,	Summons, *see Forms under Sec.* 95
,,	Order, *see Forms under Sec.* 96
108	*See Forms under Sec.* 93
110	*Forms under Secs.* 93-109 *adapted to Nuisances on Ships or Vessels, to order*

KNIGHT & CO. 90 FLEET STREET.

FIG. 1. The Marketing of Nuisance form letters, offered here by Knight and Co., in lots of one hundred, testifies both to the magnitude of policing and to the range of nuisances targeted by inspectors. From End Matter, p. 10, in F. R. Wilson, *A Practical Guide for Inspectors of Nuisances* (London, 1881).

sorts of forms that were sold to sanitary authorities by Charles Knight, the principal publisher of manuals of local government (Figure 1).

The grand and permanent problem of nuisances inspection was that of what standards of amenity to enforce. There was scope for enormous latitude, for permanent activism or wholesale complacency. F. R. Wilson, inspector for the Alnwick, Northumberland Rural Sanitary Authority, noted in his 1880 manual for inspectors, that:

> when the urban inspector finds all the sewers and drains in good working order, all the courts and yards paved and lime-washed, every house supplied with water and kept free from damp by efficient guttering and spouting, cellar dwellings—if not abolished in every instance—at least rendered as light and dry as possible, all slaughter-houses,

Leonard Shoreditch. Report of the Medical Officer of Health on the Duties of Sanitary Inspectors (London, 1869), pp. 11–12.

ashpits, and privies kept a proper distance from habitations, he may consider himself at liberty to attack more special evils, which, it is not too much to say, he will speedily be able to find.

Wilson does not say what comprises this second level of nuisances. Elsewhere, however, he suggests that nuisances inspectors might require the provision of an indoor water supply:

It is difficult to think of a greater general blessing to this country than the small matter of a water-tap in every house, or in every room used as a complete residence; for it is not too much to say that dirt is the cause of many diseases. If there were facilities for *everyone* to wash his entire body every twenty-four hours as systematically as he breaks his fast, there could not fail to be a marked improvement in the health of the population. And the mere getting rid of the unnecessary fatigue and exposure of carrying buckets of water would be another source of health.[17]

As a profession without apprenticeship, formal education, requirement for credentials, or professional organization, nuisance inspectors necessarily relied on some more arbitrary standards—their own, those of their community expressed in public opinion or local by-laws, those of a medical officer, of an appointing board, or some mix of many of these reflecting the distribution of local political power. Some kinds of nuisances were susceptible to explicit standards. On lodging houses, for example, Wilson held that unmarried males and females could not share a bed (unless both were under 10 years of age), and that apartments with married couples must have 'screens or partitions the length and breadth of each bed, and [be] of sufficient height to ensure that the occupants of it cannot be overlooked from any other bed'. But, as to what constituted an unfit dwelling, he was necessarily more vague. A dwelling 'dark, damp, low, ruinous, decaying, with bad walls and floors and roofs' was unfit for occupation.[18] To guide his colleagues, Wilson offered a general principle of utility—'the general good is desired by the legislature, i.e. the greatest amount of good to the greatest number of persons'. He also urged diplomacy. The inspector should 'make the necessary inquiries with all courtesy. He should remember that as he represents the law he is as the strong to the weak. Good humour, good words, forbearance, explicitness of explanation and clearness of instruction, will be found most serviceable'.[19]

This provides the context for the two parliamentary returns which are examined here. The first of these is a return of 1 July 1873 'showing . . . the Appointments of the several Medical Officers of Health and Inspectors of Nuisances now acting under the General Sanitary Acts, or any Local Act'.[20] It was also concerned with pluralism in such appointments—the data were to be broken down to show cases in which one person served more than one sanitary authority. The return gives the inspector's name, the area and population of the district of the appointment, the salary, the term of the appointment (the length of contract and/or

[17] F. R. Wilson, *A Practical Guide for Inspectors of Nuisances* (London, 1881), pp. 22, 88.
[18] Ibid., pp. 101–7.
[19] Ibid., p. 23.
[20] *Return of Appointments of Medical Officers of Health and Inspectors of Nuisances under the General Sanitary Acts or Local Act*, P.P. 1873 (359), LIX.

circumstances in which the inspector may be discharged), the date of the appointment of that person to the post, the act under which the appointment was made, whether the appointment was to be understood as a full-time position, and whether it was partially subsidized by the LGB, in which case there would be restrictions on the circumstances of appointment and dismissal. The return also indicates whether the urban sanitary authority is a town council, an improvement commission, or a local board. The data are divided into urban and rural sanitary authorities, and within each category ordered by county, first for England, and then for Wales. This article is concerned only with urban sanitary authorities in both England and Wales.

The second database is entitled 'Return showing with respect to the several Urban and Rural Sanitary Authorities in England and Wales . . . the several Nuisances reported to and dealt with by them in the Year ended 31 December 1874'.[21] A second portion of the return lists the costs of sanitary works undertaken during that year by these authorities. The report was presented on 11 August 1875. With regard to the nuisances, the return lists the number reported, the number abated 'without formal notice', the number of 'formal notices given', the number abated after formal notice but before 'proceedings' were taken, the number of cases 'in which proceedings were taken', the number 'abated after proceedings', and the 'total number abated'.

The two databases do not fully overlap. There are some towns which reported the appointment of a nuisances inspector, but failed to report on nuisances a year and a half later. And there are a few of the latter reports, which are not matched by any of the former. Omitting such incomplete cases still leaves 511 extra-metropolitan urban sanitary authorities. Of these, the sanitary authorities in 142 were boroughs, in 41 were improvement commissions, and in 328 were local boards. They are concentrated in Lancashire (73) and the West Riding (73).[22] To these data were added two additional variables. One is region: Wales; East Anglia; Home Counties and Southeast; Lancashire and Northwest; Yorkshire and Northeast; Midlands; and West and South. The second, potentially more troublesome, is town type: suburb, manufacturing, resort, mining, port, market, and ecclesiastical/educational/political (places such as Winchester, Ely, and Cambridge). Towns were categorized according to the descriptions in N. E. S. A. Hamilton's *National Gazetteer of Great Britain and Ireland*, which appeared volume by volume in the mid-1860s. Like Samuel Lewis's *Topographical Dictionary of England*, on which it is based (and which was used as a supplement), Hamilton gives succinct

[21] *Return from the Urban and Rural Sanitary Authorities in England and Wales of Nuisances reported and dealt with, and Estimated Cost of Sanitary Structural Works, 1874*, P.P. 1875 (434), LXIV.

[22] V. D. Lipman, *Local Government Areas, 1834–1945* (Oxford, 1949), p. 81, cites Farr's 1873 list of urban sanitary authorities. There were 721, of which 146 were municipal boroughs, and 88 improvement commissions. An 1880 return, however, cites 964 Urban Sanitary Districts, including 227 boroughs, 49 administered by improvement acts, and 688 local boards. Both figures include the Metropolis. The causes of this discrepancy are not clear, but presumably are due in part to changes during the decade. See *Return showing the present number and names of the several Urban Sanitary Authorities in England and Wales under the Public Health Act, 1875*, P.P. 1880 session 2 (388), LXI, p. 2.

descriptions of almost all of the towns on the databases, along with comments on major forms of industry.[23]

It is important to keep in mind that these are records of sanitary activity, not sanitary condition. We should not expect that twice as many nuisances in one town as another of identical size means that the former is twice as insanitary as the latter in some objective sense. It may reflect sensibilities twice as sharp, an inspector better paid and twice as energetic, or simply a different sanitary agenda. But it would be equally absurd to assume an equality of physical condition in all towns. One object of categorization by town type is to recognize that different sorts of towns faced different sorts of sanitary problems. A high rate of nuisances in a mining town dominated by a single firm, or a manufacturing town dominated by a single industry is likely to represent a quite different mode of sanitary policing than a high rate in a new suburb, a resort, or a town that saw itself as a centre of learning, law, or ecclesiastical business. In the latter context, it is likely that nuisances were being identified in the pursuit of new standards of environmental amenity rather than in safeguarding a population from epidemic disease, or even distributing new forms of environmental justice.

Parts of this study depend on the ability to arrive at a reasonably satisfactory classification of towns. This is problematic both because towns were not monolithic and because some were changing during the period. Such problems arise in perhaps a quarter of the cases. In most others, the designation is unambiguous. This is particularly the case with manufacturing and mining towns in the north and market towns in the south. In general, towns are categorized by the primary industry of the town, which Hamilton often identifies with such phrases as 'the majority of the inhabitants are occupied in the . . .'. However, in cases where a town's aspirations were prominent, either toward becoming a resort or maintaining an environment of gentility suitable to an academic or clerical town, this rule has been altered. There are several cases, for example, of towns that had been minor ports seeking to become sea-bathing resorts. Other occupations and industries might still predominate, yet it is likely that the demands of tourism brought heightened environmental standards. Certainly G. W. Wigner's systematic analysis of water quality in English seaside resorts in the late 1870s elicited a hypersensitivity to hygienic reputation.[24] One other caveat: to the extent that there is a catchall category, it is 'market'. Included under this heading are towns with no single dominant industry. Some had no formal markets, yet presumably served as general centres of commerce for an agricultural hinterland.[25]

[23] N. E. S. A. Hamilton, *National Gazetteer of Great Britain and Ireland*, 12 vols (London, n.d.); S. Lewis, *A Topographical Dictionary of England*, 7th edn, 4 vols (London, 1849). These directories appear to have been compiled mainly for clergymen interested in the living. Historical and ecclesiastical issues dominate; social and economic aspects usually get only a few lines. Twenty-three towns either could not be identified in these works or were not described sufficiently fully to be categorized.

[24] G. W. Wigner, 'On the Water Supply of Seaside Water-Places', *Sanitary Record*, 7 (1877), 117–9, 133–5, 149–52, 165–8, 181–4, 197–9, 213–16, 229–32, 245–7, 261–2, 293–6, 309–10, 325–7, 341–4, 357–60, 389–91, 417–19.

Analysis: Population and Nuisances

Not surprisingly, there is a fairly strong correlation between population and number of nuisances. Overall this is .85; for the 142 metropolitan boroughs it is .86; for 41 improvement commission-governed towns it is .74; for 328 local boards it is .43 (Table 1, column 1). These boroughs (mean population 37,520) were much larger than the places governed by local boards (mean population 6,942). They were also identifying nuisances at a greater rate. The median persons per nuisance for boroughs and improvement commissions are 74 and 73 respectively, whilst the median for local boards was 96 (Table 1, column 2). The lower correlation among local boards may reflect the greater difficulty in summoning sufficient administrative competence, energy and resources in small places, as well as the fact that those places which adopted the Public Health Act or its successors ranged from early adopters, which may be supposed to have been quite keen on sanitary activism, to those which adopted it in the 1860s as a way to circumvent potentially more onerous union-based sanitary administration.[26] Of course, the lower rate at which nuisances were being identified may also simply suggest that conditions were, or seemed, less threatening in these generally smaller places.

Breakdowns of these and other data by local government mode, region, and town type are given in column 1 of Table 1.

Overall, in English and Welsh towns there was a striking tendency to identify nuisances at roughly the same rate, although that unity disguises diversity. Noteworthy is that, generally, there is a higher correlation when the data are broken down by region than by town type. To some degree, of course, region will be a proxy for town type. Thus, most of the towns in Lancashire and the North West are Lancashire mill towns.[27] One may also be seeing regionally specific regimes of sanitary policing—towns in an area sharing experiences, determining standards, perhaps even competing in subtle ways. Yet there are also reasons to be unsurprised by the lower correlations in certain kinds of town. Mining towns, for example, might more likely be dominated by single landowners, who might either be interested, or defiantly uninterested in sanitary policing, and the same may account for the great variability in manufacturing districts. These data do seem to support the hypothesis that nuisances enforcement was being used in places

[25] For example, see Lewis' description of Thirsk, here classified as a market town even though it has other industries: 'A small quantity of coarse linen and sacking is manufactured. One of the stations on the Great Northern Railway is situated about a mile from the town. The market is on Monday, and is a large one for provisions, of which great quantities purchased here are carried for sale to Leeds and other places'. (*Topographical Dictionary*, vol. 4, s.v. 'Thirsk'.)

[26] Following the Webbs, many have argued that, between 1858 and 1862, many smaller places adopted the Public Health Act to avoid highway rating. See, for example, Finer, *English Local Government*, p. 88; R. Gutchen, 'The Genesis of the Local Government Board, 1858–71' (unpublished Ph.D. thesis, Columbia University, 1966), p. 51. Lipman (*Local Government Areas, 1834–1945*, p. 57) argues that this phenomenon has been overstated. Nonetheless, it should be kept in mind that some 'urban sanitary districts' are hardly urban in any strong sense.

[27] Unfortunately, the numbers and distribution of the towns do not allow the imposition of a standardized distribution of town types to correct the regional distribution for the influence of town type.

TABLE 1. *Nuisances and population (by government mode, region, and town type)*

	1. Correlation. number of nuisances:population	2. Persons per nuisance	
1. All towns (*n* = 511)	.85	median	89
		mean	120
		sd	834
2. Metropolitan boroughs (*n* = 142)	.86	median	74
		mean	102
		sd	1,506
3. Improvement commissions (*n* = 41)	.74	median	73
		mean	107
		sd	134
4. Local boards (*n* = 328)	.43	median	96
		mean	131
		sd	404
5. Wales (*n* = 39)	.77	median	53
		mean	102
		sd	620
6. East Anglia (*n* = 35)	.80	median	97
		mean	185
		sd	380
7. Home Counties and SE (*n* = 65)	.80	median	92
		mean	151
		sd	463
8. Lancs and NW (*n* = 100)	.96	median	94
		mean	125
		sd	207
9. Yorkshire and NE (*n* = 118)	.75	median	103
		mean	122
		sd	173
10. West and South (*n* = 74)	.90	median	89
		mean	132
		sd	654
11. Midlands (*n* = 80)	.94	median	52
		mean	79
		sd	1,902
12. Suburb (*n* = 23)	.19***	median	84
		mean	122
		sd	303
13. Manufacturing (*n* = 146)	.82	median	94
		mean	114
		sd	1,402
14. Market (*n* = 136)	.31	median	98
		mean	137
		sd	431
15. Resort (*n* = 40)	.56	median	76
		mean	149
		sd	600
16. Port (*n* = 56)	.93	median	99
		mean	142
		sd	539
17. Mining and metallurgy (*n* = 65)	.35*	median	66
		mean	90
		sd	359
18. Ecclesiastical and educational (*n* = 22)	.76	median	87
		mean	151
		sd	253

All correlations are significant at .001, except those designated: * = significant at .01 but not at .001.
All means are 5 per cent trimmed means (highest and lowest 5 per cent removed).

concerned with amenities: resorts, suburbs, and educational and ecclesiastical towns had lower persons/nuisance medians than all but mining towns. Low correlations for suburbs and resorts may reflect the mixed character of these districts, the fact that often only some parts of them were for these purposes, and hence there was a much greater variety of the effect of those parts on the rest of the town. Particularly with resorts, where a significant portion of the population was only resident for part of the year, they may also reflect variability in how population was estimated.[28] It is striking, however, that nuisances were being identified more intensively in resorts and mining towns (medians are 76 and 66 persons/nuisance) than in the others (where medians range from 84 to 99). When one turns to regions, nuisances were being identified at a greater rate in Wales and the Midlands (medians are 52 and 53), while the median town in other regions identified nuisances at a rate between 89 and 103 persons/nuisance. This too may reflect the influence of mining and metallurgy in those places, and the presence of towns with little in the way of a middle class.

Analysis: Salaries and Nuisances

For all towns the mean salary of a nuisances inspector was £40 per year (median £25) with a standard deviation of £102 (see Table 2, column 1). Mean annual salaries for manufacturing, suburbs, resorts, ecclesiastical and educational towns, and ports ranged from £48 to £58. Salaries in market towns and in mining towns were much lower, at £23 and £40. There is less variation by regions, with salaries highest in Lancashire and the Northwest (mean £55) and lowest in Wales (mean £29). These figures are more interesting when corrected for population, by considering the correlation between salary and population (Table 2, column 2) and calculating the population per pound of salary paid for nuisances inspection (Table 2, column 3). With regard to the former, there is a correlation between salary and population overall, but only of .64. This is less striking than that between population and nuisances. By region, it ranged from a low of .52 in Wales to a high of .86 in the Home Counties and the South East, and by town type from .36 for market towns to .91 for resort towns. With regard to the latter, for all towns the trimmed mean was 317 persons per pound, with a median of 263. There is little variation by region, but variation is considerable by town type. If we consider this figure as the number of residents a nuisances inspector was required to look after per pound of salary, it would appear that those employed by resorts (175) or suburbs (199) were vastly better paid than those in ecclesiastical-educational towns (mean of 509), or port towns (450). For an equal salary, a nuisance inspector in the median port town would be expected to look after roughly two and a half times as many people as if he were working in a resort town.

One thing that this probably shows is bewilderment among towns about what sort of post this was to be, and what would be the appropriate pay scale. Rather

[28] I thank an anonymous referee for raising this point.

Table 2. *Salaries and nuisances (by government mode, region, and town type)*

	1. Mean salary	2. Correlation. salary: population	3. Population/£ salary		4. Correlation. salary:nuisances (controlled for population)
1. All towns (*n* = 511)	£40	.64	median	263	.26
			mean	317	
			sd	974	
2. Metropolitan boroughs (*n* = 142)	£69	.61	median	348	.30
			mean	423	
			sd	1,805	
3. Improvement commissions (*n* = 41)	£40	.67	median	220	.16***
			mean	281	
			sd	199	
4. Local boards (*n* = 328)	£30	.62	median	230	.17*
			mean	280	
			sd	265	
5. Wales (*n* = 39)	£29	.52*	median	294	.31**
			mean	308	
			sd	198	
6. East Anglia (*n* = 35)	£42	.80	median	274	.42**
			mean	343	
			sd	264	
7. Home Counties and SE (*n* = 65)	£35	.86	median	252	.68
			mean	271	
			sd	2,594	
8. Lancs and NW (*n* = 100)	£55	.68	median	244	.23
			mean	286	
			sd	338	
9. York and NE (*n* = 118)	£36	.65	median	292	−.37
			mean	366	
			sd	415	
10. West and South (*n* = 74)	£32	.59	median	327	−.16**
			mean	323	
			sd	278	
11. Midlands (*n* = 80)	£45	.62	median	234	−.10**
			mean	304	
			sd	310	
12. Suburb (*n* = 23)	£53	.56	median	202	.33***
			mean	199	
			sd	118	
13. Manufacturing (*n* = 146)	£48	.76	median	292	.60
			mean	372	
			sd	324	
14. Market (*n* = 136)	£23	.36	median	223	.33
			mean	261	
			sd	208	
15. Resort (*n* = 40)	£48	.91	median	123	.50***
			mean	175	
			sd	149	
16. port (*n* = 56)	£58	.66	median	368	−.27
			mean	450	

(*Table continued*)

TABLE 2. *Continued*

	1. Mean salary	2. Correlation. salary: population	3. Population/£ salary		4. Correlation. salary:nuisances (controlled for population)
			sd	2,711	
17. Mining and metallurgy ($n = 65$)	£40	.66	median	222	.07***
			mean	310	
			sd	263	
18. Ecclesiastical and educational ($n = 22$)	£53	.75	median	365	.02***
			mean	509	
			sd	663	

All correlations are significant at .001, except those designated: * = significant at .01 but not at .001,** = significant at .05 but not .01, *** = not significant ($p > .05$). All means are 5 per cent trimmed means (highest and lowest 5 per cent removed).

than estimating the magnitude of the job or the kinds of experience needed to carry it out adequately, towns were copying one another or responding to even more amorphous stimuli, such as the munificence (or, more likely, tightfistedness) of the authority. At least with respect to suburbs and resorts, these data are consistent with the view that nuisances inspection had privileged status where environmental amenities might be expected to be important. Here too, the low figure in mining towns may indeed reflect the relative absence of a middle class and a high degree of real sanitary problems.

Was it the case that towns, in effect, paid for nuisances—that the more they paid the inspector, the more nuisances he identified? There is indeed a stronger correlation between salary and number of nuisances (.7 for all cases) than between salary and population (.64). When population is controlled for, the positive correlation between salary and number of nuisances is .26 (Table 2, column 4). In other words, regardless of population, towns that paid more reported more.

What this means is not wholly clear. There are two obvious possibilities. It might be argued that towns somehow sensed how large a nuisance problem they had to deal with and allocated funds accordingly; namely, that salaries depended on nuisances. Alternatively, one could argue that nuisances inspectors worked as hard as they were paid to; namely, that nuisances depended on salaries, and that towns that paid well did so because they wanted a rigorous regime of enforcement. It is the case that nuisances inspection was generally a part-time activity—the median salary of £25 would suggest that, and it is confirmed by the Parliamentary return. But unfortunately, while the return indicates whether full-time work is expected (rarely the case), it does not indicate *how much time* the part-timer was expected to devote. Consistent with both alternatives is the existence of a backlog of excess nuisances ready to be identified as soon as someone was available to spend the time identifying them.

The strength of this correlation of salary and nuisances identified (controlled for population) varies remarkably, both by region and town type. It was highest in the Home Counties, but was actually negative in three regions: in Yorkshire, where the correlation is −.37, in the West and South, where it is −.16, and in the Midlands, where it is −.1. Among town types, it is .6 in manufacturing towns and .5 in resorts. There is almost no correlation at all in mining and in ecclesiastical towns, and a −.27 correlation in port towns. And even when the problematic case of Liverpool is omitted (where the full salary is not listed), the correlation in port-towns is still −.06. In short, in some kinds of places and in some regions, nuisance inspectors produced more for less pay. The most immediate interpretation of this is that it reflects the physical conditions of towns. It shows us towns where one need not look very hard for nuisances. It may also show towns too poor to pay their staff well, and a labour market such that they could find active inspection at a low rate.

Analysis: Impact of Circumstances of Appointment

On the front lines of sanitary policing, the nuisances inspectors were likely to find themselves in the position of offending owners of property, some of whom would have influence with the employing sanitary authority. One might therefore expect a greater activism among those inspectors with longer-term appointments than those whose appointments were 'at the pleasure of the board'.[29] While one should not overestimate the job security of any local civil servant of the period, in 250 towns the inspectors served either at pleasure or in less than one-year appointments, while in 245 they had at least a one-year appointment. For those with low job security, the mean population/nuisance ratio was 138, the median 99; for those with higher job security it was 103 and 79 (Table 3). Thus, those with more apparent security were identifying nuisances at a higher rate. But the interpretation is complicated by the fact that most of the one-year appointments had been taken in the previous year in response to the new 1872 Public Health Act in places which probably hitherto had no such officer. The mean tenure of those on short security appointments was 3.1 years; that of longer security appointments 0.6 years (with a median of 0 years prior service). The new LGB was urging greater security of tenure for local inspectors and medical officers in an effort to permit them more independence of action, even offering to pay half the salary in exchange for a veto power over appointment and discharge—an offer which, in the case of inspectors of nuisances, few authorities had chosen to accept. It may well be that the higher rate of nuisances productivity among these new officers is less representative of greater job security than it is of the need to catch up, to deal with blatant problems that their longer-serving colleagues had already addressed.

Analysis: Wealth and Nuisances

The relation between the relative wealth of towns and the identification of nuisances warrants investigation but is problematic in numerous ways. Simply in

[29] Wohl, *Endangered Lives*, pp. 189–92.

TABLE 3. *Length of tenure and security of tenure*

	1. Population/ nuisances security <1 year ($n = 250$)	2. Population/ nuisances security ≥1 year ($n = 245$)	3. Mean length of tenure, short security (yrs)	4. Mean length of tenure long security (yrs)*
All towns	138 mn 99 mdn	103 mn 79 mdn	3.1	.6 mn 0 mdn
Wales	**	53 mn 39 mdn	0	1.9
East Anglia	259 mn 106 mdn	106 mn 84 mdn	2.1 mn 1 mdn	1.8
Home Counties and SE	168 mn 102 mdn	139 mn 79 mdn	2.7 mn 1 mdn	0.1
Lancs and NW	124 mn 96 mdn	126 mn 94 mdn	3.8 mn 3 mdn	0.1
York and NE	138 mn 109 mdn	107 mn 93 mdn	2.5 mn 1 mdn	0.3
West and South	236 mn 121 mdn	105 mn 77 mdn	4.2 mn 4 mdn	1.6
Midlands	90 mn 52 mdn	74 mn 53 mdn	3.1 mn 2 mdn	1.4
Suburbs	203 mn 102 mdn	47 mn 26 mdn	3.4 mn 1 mdn	0.6
Manufacturing	126 mn 103 mdn	102 mn 77 mdn	3.7 mn 2 mdn	0.5
Market	159 mn 106 mdn	125 mn 92 mdn	2.9 mn 1 mdn	0.3
Resort	366 mn 123 mdn	86 mn 71 mdn	2.6 mn 1 mdn	0.9
Port	147 mn 97 mdn	158 mn 100 mdn	3.4 mn 2 mdn	0.5
Mining and metallurgy	89 mn 77 mdn	83 mn 64 mdn	2.5 mn 1 mdn	0.3
Ecclesiastical & educational	167 mn 121 mdn	146 mn 81 mdn	4.0 mn 2 mdn	0.9

All means are 5 per cent trimmed means, *median is 0 in all breakdowns, **only 4 cases.

terms of physical conditions, it seems reasonable to expect that poorer towns would have many more things that needed fixing. With regard to administration, however, one might expect that poorer towns would have greater difficulty implementing effective inspection. Wealthier towns might be expected to be more protective of their environmental amenity; they might also have within them poorer areas with significant problems.[30] There is also the problem of a satisfactory measure of town wealth. An 1880 Parliamentary return provides figures for

[30] I thank an anonymous referee for raising the latter point. For an example of intensive nuisances-enforcement in a wealthy district, see E. Lankester, *Report of the Medical of Officer of Health made to the Vestry of St James's Westminster for the Year 1859.* London Metropolitan Archives [LMO], 70.901 (St. J). Most nuisances inspectors reported only a few classes of nuisances; James Morgan, offers 105 categories for 877 nuisances, suggesting an uncommon punctiliousness—at least in record-keeping.

rateable value. This measure, although often used by the LGB, and even by local authorities to suggest wealth, is of questionable use given variation in the means of its calculation. Estimated annual rental, listed in the same return, seems likely to be better, and is used here.[31] Still, both measures are subject to a bias induced by inclusion of industrial property: a town's annual rental may be high while most of its residents are poor if that figure includes industrial plant.

There is, however, no significant correlation between the rate at which nuisances are identified in a population and the rental per capita. Even when broken down between poor towns (ratio of population to rental value greater than .3), rich towns (less than .15), and towns in a midway position (.15–.3), there are no significant correlations in any of these groups.

Analysis: Resolution of Nuisance Cases

Almost everywhere, the great majority of the nuisance cases were reported as resolved (97 per cent), and almost always before legal proceedings were taken. Only 0.84 per cent of identified nuisances were contested legally, and the median town took no proceedings. One is led to believe that when a nuisances inspector pointed out something that needed fixing, the parties responsible did so. This is consistent with what Kearns found for Islington in the 1840s, and it occurred despite continuing ambiguity in the law on such matters as whether owner or occupier should be proceeded against.[32] The data give us some sense of how much formal pressure an inspector had to bring. Overall 39 per cent of nuisances were abated without any formal notice being given, 52 per cent after a formal notice. There is some variation in these figures. In Lancashire, the tendency was to move immediately to formal notices—60 per cent, in contrast with only 47 per cent in the West and South. Among town types, ecclesiastical and educational towns resolved things informally in only 27 per cent of cases, whilst 52 per cent of cases were resolved informally in suburbs (See Table 4). The interpretation is also made difficult by the fact that different inspectors may have meant different things by 'formal notice'.[33] What was meant by legal proceedings was much less ambiguous.

Evidently the inspectors did not have to struggle for authority against a hostile populace, but what made so many people such good citizens is unclear. That inspectors' pronouncements should be so rarely contested, even when they put owners or occupiers to trouble and expense, suggests either great acceptance of the sanitary idea (and inspectors' expertise in embodying it) or the degree to which people would go to avoid being branded as 'dirty'. In his 1856 cholera novel, *Two Years Ago*, Charles Kingsley suggested that the motive force of

[31] *Return showing the present number and names of the several Urban Sanitary Authorities in England and Wales under the Public Health Act, 1875*, P.P. 1880 session 2 (388), LXII.

[32] Kearns, 'Cholera, Nuisances, and Environmental Management in Islington'.

[33] Partly for this reason, I have not utilized the more complex breakdown of modes of resolution given in the original return.

TABLE 4. *Modes of nuisance resolution*

	Per cent resolved	Proceedings (%)	Abated without formal notice	Abated after formal notice
All towns	97	0.8	39	52
Wales	95	1.7	35	55
East Anglia	95	0.7	43	48
Home Counties and SE	98	0.5	43	51
Lancs and NW	95	0.9	30	59
York and NE	96	1.1	42	50
West and South	97	0.4	45	47
Midlands	97	0.9	37	54
Suburbs	100	1.2	52	44
Manufacturing	97	0.8	37	55
Market	96	0.7	43	47
Resort	98	0.4	42	52
Port	97	0.8	34	59
Mining and metallurgy	96	1.7	39	51
Ecclesiastical & educational	96	0.6	27	66

household sanitary improvement was humiliation—the satisfaction of inflicting it; the efforts, either by denial or quiet acquiescence, to avoid it.[34]

Analysis: Impact of Town Size

It has also proved intriguing to explore how these relationships change when the towns are broken down into the classes of small (population <5,000), medium (5,000–50,000), and large (>50,000). There are 231 towns in the first class, 253 in the second, and 27 in the third. This gives us one way to look for asymmetries in the distribution of some factors.

In small towns (median population 3,050), the mean salary was £17 with a median of £10; the mean annual total of nuisances was 52 and the median 31. In medium towns (median population 10,500), the mean salary was £53 and the median £50, the mean annual total of nuisances 240, and the median 142. For the large towns (median population 90,007), the mean salary was £150 and the median £100. The mean annual nuisances was 4,920 and the median 1,967. Resolution practices were roughly similar. In the median large town 0.49 per cent of cases went to law; in the median medium town the figure was even smaller at 0.28; in the median small town no cases went to law. But smaller towns, not surprisingly, were less formal. In the median small town, 43 per cent of cases were abated without formal notice. Analogous figures are 35 per cent for medium towns, but only 7 per cent in large towns.

These figures suggest that inspectors in larger towns were closer to sharing a routine with one another. They were identifying about 80 per cent more nuisances per person than their colleagues in smaller places, but having to look

[34] C. Kingsley, *Two Years Ago* (New York, 1908), vol. 1, ch. 18.

TABLE 5. *Towns by size classes*

	1. Median population	2. Mean and median salary	3. Nuisances	4. % of cases in which proceedings taken, median	5. % of cases abated without formal notice	6. Correlation. number of nuisances: population	7. Correlation. salary: population	8. Correlation. salary: nuisances (controlled for population)	9. Population/ nuisances	10. Population/ £ salary
Small towns	3050	17 mn	52 mn	0	43	.21	.23	.31	130 mn	269 mn
<5000		10 mdn	31 mdn						92 mdn	225 mdn
(*n* = 231)									415 sd	243 sd
Medium towns	10,500	53 mn	240 mn	.28	35	.35	.51	.14	118 mn	330 mn
>5000 ≤50,000		50 mdn	142 mdn						91 mdn	278 mdn
(*n* = 253)									1,100 sd	1,355 sd
Large towns	90,007	150 mn	4,920 mn	.49	7	.88	.44**	.33	70 mn	661 mn
>50,000		100 mdn	1,967 mdn						48 mdn	647 mdn
(*n* = 27)									653 sd	496 sd

All correlations are significant at .001, except those designated: * = significant at .01 but not at .001, ** = significant at .05 but not .01, *** = not significant ($p > .05$). All means are 5 per cent trimmed means (highest and lowest 5 per cent removed).

after nearly twice as many per pound of their salary. To some degree, the concentration of nuisances identification in large places is exactly what one might expect: the environmental nuisance is quintessentially a phenomenon of concentration. The great discrepancy of persons per pound in nuisances administration is distorted by two factors: one is that even small places probably found it impossible to continue to reduce salary proportionately to population. Nuisances inspectors might be part-time, but they could not, after all, be subdivided. Every urban sanitary district had to meet a threshold cost of getting someone to take the post. At the other end of the scale, it is likely that, in very large places, the official nuisances inspector had assistants, including policemen. There are some places where this was clearly the case; their impact will be discussed below.

Analysis: Maxima and Minima

Whilst it is the virtue of statistics to steer us away from the remarkable cases that would otherwise preoccupy us, it is intriguing nonetheless to examine which towns had the most and fewest nuisances per capita. The ten most nuisance-intensive towns were Blackpool, Bulith, Hanley, Houghton-le-Spring (in Durham), Swinton and Pendlebury (outside Salford), Audley, Darlaston, Hardingstone (Northampton), Cramlington (Northumberland), and Jarrow. In Blackpool, there was a nuisance discovered for every 2.24 persons; in Jarrow, one for every 7.46. Blackpool was a resort, six of the others were mining and metallurgical towns, and three were market towns. At the nuisance-free end of the scale, we find Glossop, Swindon, Plymouth, Littlehampton, Bryn Mawr, Ryde, Howdon, Romford, Brierfield, and Ham Common. The persons per nuisance there range from 17,000 to 1 in the case of Glossop and 1,153 to 1 in the case of Ham Common. Three of these were market towns, one (Glossop) was a manufacturing town, two were ports, two were resorts, one was a mining town, and Ham Common was a suburb.

Conclusion

The value of this analysis depends on the credibility of the data and their typicality. Both are problematic, although not sufficiently so to compromise the general utility of the findings.

Credibility

Can we believe these data? In general, the answer is ‘yes’. Although the survival of the books of nineteenth-century nuisances inspectors is uneven, those that have survived indicate that the inspectors recorded the sorts of details (on such matters as the number and resolution of nuisance cases) that Whitehall requested for the returns.[35] Reported salary figures are in the same range as those from other

[35] Good examples of surviving inspectors’ books are the Hendon Local Board Complaint Books for 1879–85, LMA 4048; the Inspector’s report books for St George’s in the East and for Poplar,

sources. Still, with regard to nuisance numbers and salaries, there are some potential problems in the data sets that need to be mentioned.

In the case of salary figures, cases have not been included in which a listed salary was only partially for inspecting nuisances; namely, in cases when the inspector doubled as collector or surveyor. Unfortunately we cannot be sure that the compilers of the tables were uniformly informed of such cases. There are also a few cases where the salary is listed as zero or nil, but an appointee is mentioned, and some number of nuisances cited. In such cases it seems right to assume that the duties have simply been added to another post. Such cases have been omitted. They were common in Cornwall, which is accordingly underrepresented here. In a few cases, a weekly or even a daily salary was given. This has been calculated on an annual basis, even though one cannot be sure that nuisances inspection was being done year-round.

Another possibility is that more persons and money were being devoted to nuisances inspection in some towns than is listed on the reports. Some responses, most notably that of Manchester, include the names and salaries of the full staff of 15 men. Their total salary is £1,897 and they identified 50,514 nuisances. For Liverpool, by contrast, only the designated inspector is listed, at a salary of £220. It is not credible that this single individual should have identified 44,966 nuisances in that same year. There are 28 places with more than 1,000 nuisances in a year. The median population of these places is 76,400 and the median salary is £120, the mean £213. These include both towns where multiple staff are acknowledged and those where they are not. How serious a problem this is, is not clear. It does seem likely that in smaller towns the designated inspector was probably the single nuisances regulation official. A preliminary inspection of medical officers' reports for metropolitan district boards and parishes suggests that a single inspector was the norm until the mid-1880s, even for these very large districts. Often the achievements of these single officers were indeed prodigious.

With regard to the reports of nuisances, the problem is that of cases in which the number of nuisances abated exceeds the number reported to exist in the first place. Sometimes it is only slightly greater, but one sometimes finds that no nuisances have been reported, but a great number abated. There appear three likely sources for such irregularities. First, some cases may reflect clerical errors in the multiple redactions of these data. Secondly, in some cases, particularly those where the difference is small, the discrepancy may reflect the fact that the calendar year of the reporting and the abating of a nuisance will not necessarily be identical: that is, at the end of any year, not all of the nuisances reported may have been abated, and at the beginning some will be in the process of abatement that were reported in the previous year. Finally, respondents may have differently interpreted what information was wanted. As noted, inspectors were both to inspect and to respond to complaints. It is possible that where the number

Bancroft Library, STE 132-6, Pop/1118; and the Sanitary Inspector's Journals for Blackpool, 1889–1905, Lancashire Record Office, Preston, Acc. 8399.

reported is zero or small, they are recording only the cases brought to their attention by others, as complaints. In such cases, the number reported has been replaced by the number abated on the grounds that a nuisance cannot be abated unless it is first identified as existing. There are 74 such cases.

Typicality

Sadly these data were not collected in further years, and the question therefore arises of whether they were typical. One reason for this is that the universal requirement for the appointment of inspectors of nuisances was new. About half the inspectors had been appointed in the preceding year. In most cases, they were probably the first appointments those towns made. We might suppose both a backlog of unmet nuisances and an eagerness to impress. On the other hand, the surviving annual reports or complaint books of inspectors suggest that activism was the norm, that sanitary expectations changed and intensified, and even that the official responsibilities of the post grew as the inspector became, in many cases, an executor of national legislative mandates. In Gateshead, Robert Nesbitt, the inspector in 1873, reported 480 nuisances; in 1903, William Jours reported 3,099. In Battersea, Isaac Young oversaw 75,553 'sanitary operations' in 1899, including 47,000 house inspections—there were only about 24,000 dwellings in the parish.[36]

As noted, these data offer us a snapshot. While there are some factors that blur the image, (chiefly variations in reporting nuisances, salaries, even population; equally the difficulties in classifying towns), there appear to be no systematic distortions and the large number of cases gives some reason for confidence. Still, we ought not to assume that the ratios that prevailed in 1873–4 would obtain a decade or two later. Mainly these data support an hypothesis of energetic, though not necessarily adequate or even efficient, sanitary policing. Although standard deviations are often high, and, on such issues as the ratio of persons per nuisance, means often significantly exceed medians, most towns were doing something more than giving lip service to Local Government Board dictates. What they were doing—what conditions constituted these thousands of nuisances—is beyond the scope of this article. So too, and even more difficult to discern, is a systematic longitudinal picture: how did the nature, as well as the number, of nuisances change from the inception of the sanitary movement in the 1840s through to its full professionalization by the end of the century? Both of these aspects are the subject of ongoing research.

Acknowledgements

I wish to thank Professors E. P. Hennock, Bill Luckin, and Graham Mooney, as well as two referees, for suggestions on data interpretation and presentation,

[36] W. Jours, *County Borough of Gateshead. The Annual Report of the Gateshead Inspector of Nuisances for the year 1903* (Gateshead, 1903), p. 13; I. Young, *Vestry of St Mary Battersea. Annual Report of the Chief Sanitary Inspector for the Year 1899*, p. 6.

Professor Felicia Le Clare and Ms Keely Jones for statistical guidance, and Katherine Hamlin for data entry.

Social History of Medicine Vol. 18 No. 1 © *The Society for the Social History of Medicine 2005, all rights reserved.*
doi:10.1093/sochis/hki007

Coming Up for Air: Experts, Employers, and Workers in Campaigns to Compensate Silicosis Sufferers in Britain, 1918–1939

By MARK W. BUFTON★ and JOSEPH MELLING★

SUMMARY. Government regulation of dangerous trades and the compensation of those injured by their work remains a matter of considerable debate among medical historians. Trade unions have frequently been criticized for pursuing financial awards for their members rather than demanding improvements in health and safety at the workplace. This article examines the neglected subject of silicosis injuries in Britain from the time when the first legislation was passed for the compensation of those suffering from the harmful affects of silica dust in 1918 to the outbreak of war in 1939, when a major new study was under way which would transform the scientific understanding and the legal compensation of those who were diagnosed as being ill with pneumoconiosis. It is argued that in framing legislation for compensation, politicians and their civil servants sought to retain the legal framework created in 1897–1906 and developed a model of industrial insurance which depended to a large extent on a co-operative relationship with leading employers. Medical scientists identified silica as a uniquely hazardous agent in workers' lung disease, while emphasizing the specialist knowledge required for its diagnosis. One remarkable feature of the selective compensation schemes devised after 1918 was the reliance on geological rather than pathological evidence to prove compensation rights, as well as strict employment limits on those eligible to claim. Only the campaigning of labour organizations and persistent evidence of lung disease among anthracite coal miners led to a significant relaxation of compensation rules in 1934 and the fresh scientific investigation which transformed the medical understanding of respiratory illness among industrial workers.

KEYWORDS: silicosis, workmen's compensation, coal, Miners' Federation, Thomas Legge, geology, asbestos, trade unions, medical expertise, twentieth century.

In November 1931, Dr Thomas Legge advised Britain's Trades Union Congress (TUC) on their attempts to secure an interview with a new committee of the Medical Research Council. The MRC's Industrial Pulmonary Diseases Committee had been established after the Mines Minister, Emmanuel Shinwell, had decided that lung diseases among Welsh coal miners required fresh investigation. As Medical Adviser to the TUC, Legge subsequently drafted a detailed letter which would express the dissatisfaction of his Council 'at being kept in the dark as to what the Committee [was] doing', particularly as they had urged on Government the previous year the urgent need for such a committee to review

★Silicosis Project and CWP Project, Wellcome Sponsored Centre for Medical History, SHIPSS, Amory Building, Exeter University, Exeter, Devon EX4 4RJ, UK. Email: M.W.Bufton@exeter.ac.uk Email: j.l.melling@exeter.ac.uk. Mark Bufton now: Honorary University Fellow, Exeter University.

the advances made in the medical understanding of respiratory diseases since the matter had been considered by the Samuel Committee of 1907.[1] This letter persuaded the Committee to reconsider their refusal to meet the TUC, although they stressed that they remained exclusively concerned with the pursuit of knowledge by scientific method rather than such contentious administrative matters as compensation for industrial diseases. It was in the interests of securing 'trustworthy data of the kind useful for scientific investigation', that they agreed to discuss matters with trade union leaders.[2]

The importance which the TUC attached to this meeting can be partly explained by the presence among its members of the leading specialists on industrial respiratory diseases, including its chair, A. J. Hall, the Senior Medical Inspector of Factories, J. C. Bridge, and its Secretary, E. L. Middleton. Legge regarded Middleton as 'the greatest authority in the country on Silicosis'.[3] The union leaders were also anxious to discover how the research agenda of the Committee would impinge on workers' statutory rights to compensation for industrial disease, more particularly the provisions made for those suffering from the harmful effects of silica, coal, and other mineral dusts. When serving as the first Factory Medical Inspector at the Home Office, Legge had reported in 1900 on the high mortality among men who mined ganister (a silica-rich fireclay), their lungs displaying the 'iron grey nodules' and serious lesions which were soon recognized as the characteristic symptoms of those suffering from the prolonged inhalation of concentrated silica dust.[4] J. S. Haldane's seminal study of lung diseases among Cornish metal miners followed in 1904. Both Legge and Haldane shared throughout their careers a conviction that it was the presence of tuberculosis which proved the lethal complication for sufferers, transforming their condition into a prolonged and fatal illness.[5] The invasion of the lung's alveoli by microscopic particles of fine silica dust gradually formed the congested areas which resulted in the fibrotic scarring of the lung tissue and the serious lesions usually associated with tuberculosis.

[1] Modern Record Centre, Warwick University, Trades Union Congress Papers [Hereafter TUC Papers], 292/144.35/1, memorandum Legge to Smyth, 19 November 1931; Walter Citrine to Walter Fletcher of MRC, 16 February 1932. Legge added in a memorandum to the TUC's Insurance Secretary that a leading member of the Medical Research Council (hereafter MRC) Committee had recently addressed a meeting of engineers in south Wales, where he had treated his audience 'very much as though they were medical men and would understand his pathological findings. I do not doubt that representatives of the miners, had they been there, would have been able to understand them quite as well.' Legge to Smyth, 17 February 1932. See The National Archives, Public Record Office, Kew (hereafter PRO), PIN 11/18, R. R. Bannatyne, memorandum, 2 September 1907, for the commentary of Thomas Legge on the 1907 Committee.

[2] TUC Papers, 292/144.35.1, Fletcher to Citrine, 11 May 1932.

[3] TUC Papers, 292/144.341/8, Legge, 'Silicosis among Coal Miners', dated 14 April 1930. This seems to have been written from notes prepared for a meeting with the MFGB held on 13 March, which was reported in a minute of 25 March 1930. Other members mentioned included A. E. Barclay, S. Lyle Cummins, and E. H. Kettle.

[4] T. M. Legge, 'Industrial Diseases Under the Workmen's Compensation Act', *Journal of Industrial Hygiene*, 1 (1920), 25–32, pp. 26, 29–30.

[5] TUC Papers, 2929/144.341/3, memorandum for Evidence of Thomas Morison Legge to the Silicosis (Medical Arrangements) Committee (1929), pp. 3–5; A. Meiklejohn, 'The Development of Compensation for Occupational Diseases of the Lungs in Great Britain', *British Journal of Industrial Medicine*, 11 (1954), 198–212, pp. 198–9.

One estimate suggested that the disease was responsible by the early 1930s for more than 300 deaths each year in England and Wales.[6]

The point which galvanized trade union leaders in major industries such as coal mining was the absence of medical explanations for the persistence of lung disorders among coal miners rather than ganister miners, sandstone quarrymen, or mineral and rock workers. Not only were there a limited number of employees who could qualify for compensation when injured by breathing in silica dust, but the pathway to financial redress clearly differed for silicosis sufferers as distinct from other occupational diseases. The rights of employees certified to be victims of this incurable, wasting disease differed not only between those included and excluded from statutory compensation, but also among the trades which were recognized to be most at risk from exposure to silica. The right to claim compensation depended on being able to prove that the affected worker had been employed on, or immediately near, rock which could be shown to be primarily made up of silica. As the original model was extended and adapted to other industries, peculiar arrangements were developed for the handling of claims by the insurance funds created to recompense the diseased worker.

It was the dissatisfaction of those excluded, such as members of the Miners' Federation of Great Britain (MFGB), which resulted in a series of challenges to the system of compensation from the passage of the Workmen's Compensation Act in 1925. Under pressure from the miners' leaders, the TUC drafted its own legislation to overhaul the system of compensation, including the provisions for those suffering from occupational illnesses. It was again the Anthracite Miners' Association of South Wales which pressed the problem of anthracosis, or coal dust inhalation, on Shinwell in 1929–30. The subsequent exchanges which took place in 1928–32 between the TUC and medical experts on the causes and extent of dust hazards at work provide an insight into the complex relationship between scientific investigation and the range of political influences which framed compensation rights in the United Kingdom during the early twentieth century.

This article examines the contribution of medical expertise to the development of statutory schemes for the compensation of industrial silicosis during the interwar years. The medical arrangements for the approval of compensation payments became the subject of intense scrutiny and debate in this period. The provisions made for the examination and certification of workers with respiratory illnesses caused by workplace dust have also been a point of debate among medical historians, as scholars have variously criticized and defended the policies adopted by the Home Office and the interpretation of these policies by senior medical personnel. Less attention has been devoted to variations in the statutory compensation schemes introduced for different industries. There were also important conflicts within the ranks of the British civil service and among members of the scientific community, who were most closely involved in the framing and application of

[6] MRC, Fourteenth Annual Report of the Industrial Health Research Board (1934), p. 11; D. Hunter, *Diseases of Occupations* (London, 6th ed.), pp. 935–7, 941, 950–1, 956–7, 962–7, 973. For a modern definition, see J. E. Parker and G. R. Wagner, 'Silicosis', in *Encyclopaedia of Occupational Health and Safety*, vol. 1 (Geneva, 1998, 4th ed.), pp. 10.1–10.97.

compensation provisions for those who had suffered from silica inhalation. The tacit scientific consensus which had emerged on the peculiar hazard posed by silica dust to the industrial worker proved surprisingly fragile as British trade unions challenged the technical and legal foundations on which the original 1919 silicosis scheme had been constructed.

It is argued here that the distinctive character of the industrial schemes that were developed after 1928 was the result of battles between different interest groups among medical and other scientific experts as well as clashes involving employers, unions, insurers, and government. For much of the impetus for investigation into pulmonary disease arose from two main sources: first, the struggle of trade unions for an extension of compensation rights; and secondly, the activities of physicians and campaigners who were primarily involved in the diagnosis, treatment, and prevention of tuberculosis. Faced with these challenges, leading medical specialists as well as civil servants sought to contain the public controversy over the origins and extent of pulmonary disease among the industrial labour force, and conceal the limits of the scientific understanding of respiratory illnesses, in a series of practical arrangements that served to shield the medical physician from legal interrogation by grounding compensation rights on the physical proximity of the employee to rock which possessed a minimum content of silica. A second important thread in the fabric of medical arrangements introduced for the certification and financial recompense of silicosis sufferers was the persistence of conflicts within the ranks of organized labour as well as among the business and scientific communities. In demanding greater access to scientific investigations into lung disease, the TUC itself faced serious criticism from coal mining unions which pressed for radical reform of silicosis compensation from 1926. We suggest that these differences reflected not only political rifts within the British unions but also the complex range of opportunities and risks which the availability of compensation presented to the unions and their members.

These points are developed in the remainder of the article. We first consider recent discussions of dust-related diseases by medical historians, followed by an examination of the origins and growth of silicosis schemes after 1918. The final part of the article considers the policies pursued by the coal mining unions and the pattern of claims for compensation made by the miners themselves during the 1930s.

Rescued by Science? Medical Experts and Compensation for Industrial Illness

There is now a substantial medical and historical literature on the tragic consequences of asbestos poisoning and the continuing rise in the incidence of lung cancer among the employees of manufacturers in that industry.[7] Episodes in scientific research and the regulation of asbestos dust, such as the publication of the

[7] See J. Peto, J. T. Hodgson, F. E. Matthews, and J. R. Jones, 'Continuing Increase in Mesothelioma Mortality in Britain', *The Lancet*, 345 (1995), 535–9; J. Peto, C. Vecchia, F. Levi, and I. Negri, 'The European Mesothelioma Epidemic', *British Journal of Cancer*, 79 (1999), 666–72; N. J. Wikeley, *Compensation for Industrial Disease* (Aldershot, 1993).

Merewether–Price Report and the introduction of statutory controls on industrial manipulation of the substance in 1930–1, have proved the subject of intense and often bitter debate among historians.[8] Peter Bartrip's recent contributions have been distinguished by the fierce critique he offers of the flawed assumptions which he finds in the research of numerous scholars who have investigated the policies of business and government in the regulation, treatment, and compensation of asbestosis.[9] Much less attention has been devoted by medical historians in Britain to the hazards of silica, although the work of Rosner, Markowitz, and others have established an impressive basis for an informed historical discussion of the disease in the United States.[10]

An important theme in the historical literature on British occupational health has been the role of trade unions in promoting safety at work. A number of authors have criticized the unions in the asbestos and other industries for pursuing compensation awards and protecting employment levels at the expense of promoting preventive safety measures in the industrial workplace.[11] Bartrip's interpretation of the close involvement of trade unions in framing the asbestos dust controls of 1931 may again be distinguished from most other historians, although his earlier studies of Workmen's Compensation legislation also suggested that the pursuit of compensation awards by the unions achieved little improvement in workplace safety.[12] Such critical views of the role of organized labour in the

[8] N. Wikely, 'The Asbestos Regulations 1931: A Licence to Kill?', *Journal of Law and Society*, 19 (1992), 365–78, pp. 373–4; D. J. Jeremy, 'Corporate Responses to the Emergent Recognition of a Health Hazard in the UK Asbestos Industry', *Business and Economic History*, 24 (1995), 254–65, p. 261; G. Tweedale, *From Magic Mineral to Killer Dust: Turner and Newall and the Asbestos Hazard* (Oxford), pp. 26, 289; G. Tweedale and D. J. Jeremy, 'Compensating the Workers: Industrial Injury and Compensation in the Asbestos Industry, 1930–1960s', *Business History*, 41 (1999), 102–20, p. 116; G. Tweedale and P. Hansen, 'Protecting the Workers: The Medical Board and the Asbestos Industry, 1930s–1960s', *Medical History*, 42 (1998), 439–57, p. 456.

[9] P. W. J. Bartrip, *The Way From Dusty Death: Turner and Newall and the Regulation of Occupational Health in the British Asbestos Industry 1890s–1970* (London, 2001), pp. 27–50, 265–6, 312–13, n. 155. See also P. W. J. Bartrip, 'Nellie Kershaw, Turner and Newall, and Asbestos-related Disease in 1920s Britain', *Historical Studies in Industrial Relations*, 9 (2000), 101–16.

[10] D. Rosner and G. Markowitz, *Deadly Dust: Silicosis and the Politics of Occupational Disease in Twentieth Century America* (Princeton, 1991); C. C. Sellers, *Hazards of the Job. From Industrial Disease to Environmental Health Science* (Chapel Hill and London, 1997), p. 331.

[11] P. Weindling, 'Linking Self Help and Medical Science: The Social History of Occupational Health', in P. Weindling (ed.), *The Social History of Occupational Health* (London 1985), 5–29, p. 10; Tweedale, *From Magic Mineral to Killer Dust*, pp. 26, 28, 170–1, 289; A. McIvor, 'Health and Safety in the Cotton Industry: A Literature Survey', *Manchester Region History Review*, 9 (1995), 50–7; M. Greenberg, 'Knowledge of the Health Hazard of Asbestos Prior to the Merewether and Price Report of 1930, *Social History of Medicine*, 7 (1994), 493–516, p. 514; A. Dalton, *Asbestos Killer Dust* (London, 1979); Tweedale and Jeremy, 'Compensating the Workers', p. 116; Wikeley, 'Asbestos Regulations', pp. 370–2, 374–5; idem, 'Turner and Newall: Early Organisational Responses to Litigation Risk', *Journal of Law and Society*, 24 (1997), 252–75, p. 268.

[12] P. W. J. Bartrip, 'Too Little, Too Late? The Home Office and the Asbestos Industry Regulations, 1931', *Medical History*, 42 (1998), 421–38. P. W. J. Bartrip and S. Burnam, *The Wounded Soldiers of Industry: Industrial Compensation Policy 1833 to 1897* (Oxford, 1983), p. 221, note somewhat opaquely that trade unions opposed the abolition of tort actions against employers 'in order to divert the money paid in employers' liability insurance premiums towards higher benefits under a no-fault scheme'. The authors suggest that safety would have been better served by investment in accident prevention than accident insurance schemes which were frequently insensitive to continuing hazards. See also

progress of industrial health and safety may be contrasted with recent research by Bowden and Tweedale into byssinosis among textile workers, which depicts the positive influence of the unions.[13] Recent econometric studies of American compensation reform similarly indicate that the strength of labour unions was positively correlated with higher levels of state compensation benefits awarded both by employers and government in the early twentieth century.[14]

The argument that British (and American) trade unions have historically displayed little interest in workplace safety and have privileged financial recompense over the prevention of accidents cannot be sustained as an accurate summary of labour attitudes and policies. Employers as well as trade unions differed in their responses to the specific proposals, usually depending on the costs and risks to output presented by the removal of hazards to the workforce. Business criticisms of Workmen's Compensation stemmed not only from considerations of cost but also the alleged impact that 'malingering' for sickness payments had upon the discipline and morale of the employees.[15] Faced with the prospect of new compensation legislation in 1906, the Coal Owners of North Wales considered the liability of older workers to accident and illness, deciding to take steps 'at all Collieries to quietly get rid of workmen over 65 years of age'.[16] Keen to remove employees who presented a bad insurance risk, the employers acknowledged that the strength and vigilance of the miners' unions prevented the compulsory medical examination of the labour force, although an increasing number of disputed cases were referred to specialist medical referees after the Act of 1906 was passed.[17]

P. W. J. Bartrip, *Workmen's Compensation in the Twentieth Century: Law, History and Social Policy* (Avebury, 1983).

[13] S. Bowden and G. Tweedale, 'Poisoned by the Fluff: Compensation and Litigation for Byssinosis in the Lancashire Cotton Industry', *Journal of Law and Society*, 29 (2002), 560–79; S. Bowden and G. Tweedale, 'Mondays without Dread: The Trade Union Response to Byssinosis in the Lancashire Cotton Industry in the Twentieth Century', *Social History of Medicine*, 16 (2003), 79–95.

[14] P. V. Fishback, *Soft Coal, Hard Choices: The Economic Welfare of Bituminous Coal Miners, 1890–1930* (New York, 1992); P. V. Fishback and S. Kantor, 'The Good, the Bad and the Paycheck: Compensating Differentials in Labor Markets, 1884–1903', *University of Arizona Economics Working Paper 91* (July 1991); P. V. Fishback and S. E. Kantor, '"Square Deal" or Raw Deal? Market Compensation for Workplace Disamenities, 1884–1903', *Journal of Economic History*, 52 (1992), 826–48; S. W. Kim and P. V. Fishback, 'Institutional Change, Compensating Differentials and Accident Risk in American Railroading, 1892–1945', *Journal of Economic History*, 53 (1993), 796–823; P. V. Fishback and S. E. Kantor, 'The Political Economy of Workmen's Compensation Benefit Levels, 1910–1930', *Explorations in Economic History*, 35 (1998), 109–139, pp. 122–3, 126–8. See also P. Dorman, *Markets and Mortality: Economics, Dangerous Work, and the Value of Human Life* (Cambridge, 1996).

[15] *Departmental Committee on Workmen's Compensation, Minutes of Evidence*, P.P. 1904 (Cd. 2334) II, p. 235, Q. 5930 for Halliday on 'malingering' of workers and p. 251, Q. 6260 for Baird on 'fortuitous' illness claims arising out of minor accidents.

[16] National Library of Wales, Aberystwyth, North Wales Coal Owners Association Committee (NWCOA), Minutes, 15 March 1906. See also *Departmental Committee on Workmen's Compensation, Minutes of Evidence*, P.P. 1904 (Cd. 2334) II, p. 249, Q. 6237. Evidence of Scottish coal owner and Secretary of Scottish Mine Owners Defence Mutual on elderly miners.

[17] NWCOA, Minutes, 24 September 1906. The Owners agreed that any doubtful cases be referred to their colliery doctors. *Workmen's Compensation, Statistics of Compensation During the Year 1911*, P.P. 1912 (Cd. 6493), pp. 14–15 show the marked rise in proceedings after 1907 with a clear decline in Employers' Liability Act cases. There were 215 English and 86 Scottish medical referees in service at the end of 1911.

The following year, a Departmental Committee considered the provision first made in the 1906 legislation for industrial diseases and proposed that to qualify for compensation an individual's illness must have demonstrably arisen as a result of a specific activity or process of production.[18] It was already apparent to the Samuel Committee that the symptoms of pulmonary disease, or 'fibroid phthisis', could be found in a number of trades where rock and stone were worked. The Committee concluded that it was impracticable to schedule such illness for compensation purposes. The slow progress of the disease and the ambivalence of its early symptoms made diagnosis difficult, roentgen X-ray examination having been established for little more than a decade. By 1918, however, Medical Factory Inspectors, such as Edgar Collis, had provided formidable evidence of an association between employment in mining and working silica-rich rock and the onset of serious lung disease.[19] The emerging medical consensus on the causes of pulmonary fibrosis among stone workers did not secure compensation for thousands of workers exposed to the dust. The Samuel Committee of 1907 had resisted the inclusion of fibroid phthisis in the schedule, partly on the grounds that the early detection of respiratory illness and the possibility that an employee might develop a disease which required substantial compensation would persuade employers to dismiss, without recompense, any worker displaying mild symptoms. The threat of unemployment would similarly discourage workers from co-operating with medical examiners or revealing details of their working careers.[20]

Legislation to compensate those suffering from the effects of silica dust was developed in the later years of the First World War, at a time when a robust consensus on the aetiology of silicosis was clearly established, including the characteristic appearance of 'nodules' of fibrous tissue in the lungs of the sufferers.[21] The experience of research and experimentation in the South African mining industry in 1910–12, followed by the institution of a contributory industrial compensation fund for the gold fields, proved an influential model for British commentators.[22] The Medical Factory Inspectorate of the Home Office and their superiors played a prominent role in the creation of the orthodox view of silicosis by 1918. They also remained committed to the principle, established in the compensation legislation of 1897–1906, that private industry should bear the financial burden of the injuries which resulted from hazardous production. The framing of compensation

[18] Samuel Committee, Report of the Departmental Committee on Compensation for Industrial Diseases, Cd. 3495, HSMO (1907) London. Also Samuel Committee, *Second Report of the Departmental Committee on Compensation for Industrial Diseases*, Cd. 4386, HSMO (1908) London.

[19] Meiklejohn, 'Development of Compensation', p. 200, claimed that Collis's Milroy Lecture of 1915 on 'Industrial Pneumoconioses' had 'the greatest influence in defining silicosis research and legislation in Britain'.

[20] T. M. Legge, 'Industrial Diseases under the Workmen's Compensation Act', *Journal of Industrial Hygiene*, 1 (1920), 25–32, p. 26.

[21] E. L. Middleton, 'The Etiology of Silicosis', *Tubercle*, 1 (1919–20), 257–62. Middleton had been employed as a Tuberculosis Officer in north Wales before working at a south Wales sanatorium and subsequently as a Medical Referee.

[22] PRO, PIN 12/11, Refractories Industries (Silicosis) Scheme, 1919. This file includes extensive notes on South Africa 'and other colonies'.

provisions in Britain depended less on the state of medical knowledge than on the fundamental principle that industrial injury was an insurable risk which should be undertaken by private firms rather than organized by the State.[23] There remained the problem of identifying a particular period of employment as the origins or cause of the injury inflicted on the employee, more particularly where a disabling disease such as silicosis had developed over a lengthy period. The difficulty was eased but not resolved by the lighter burden placed on plaintiffs under British compensation law to demonstrate the precise causal link between the onset of disease and a specific period of employment that was commonly required of claimants in many American states.[24]

One consequence of this policy principle was that the Home Office was given the responsibility of securing the co-operation of key employers as well as organized labour in the introduction of a system for examining, certifying, and compensating those who displayed symptoms. Enforcing liability on individual firms under the existing legislation was likely to prove difficult and expensive, while persuading organized employers to accept compulsion presented at least as many obstacles to politicians and civil servants. Hall and Collis discovered in 1917, for example, that employers in the ganister industry were firmly opposed to the scheduling of fibroid phthisis as an industrial disease, although willing to contemplate a voluntary insurance scheme.[25] Even less likely to co-operate in any provisions that extended the compensation terms of 1906 were the coal owners of such districts as south Wales, who frequently held the legislation responsible for a weakening of the 'moral sense' of the mining community.[26] Among the injuries and ailments scheduled as industrial diseases from 1906, those affecting coal miners accounted for the great majority of claims for which compensation was paid by 1914, although the industry was clearly excluded from silicosis provisions until 1928.[27]

The following part of the article considers the development of schemes after 1918. We suggest that the trade unions played a significant role in the public debate on pulmonary disease at work, particularly in the coal mining industry. The readiness of organized workers to challenge the technical and scientific as well as the legal criteria for compensation in these years contributed to the reappraisal of the origins and extent of industrial pneumoconiosis long before the

[23] PRO, PIN 12/11, Refractories Industries (Silicosis) Scheme 1919, Brace at Conference with trade unions, 17 July 1917.

[24] M. R. Mayers, 'Time Limitation in Compensation for Industrial Diseases', *Journal of Industrial Hygiene*, 14 (1933), 466–72, compares British and American provisions in regard to contracting disease.

[25] PRO, PIN 12/11, E. L. Collis, 'Ganister Mining', 20 April 1917, with R. R. Bannatyne marginal notes, 25 April 1917; A. J. Hall, 'Memo on Ganister Mining', 19 December 1917; Hall to Legge, 19 December 1917 and Collis note, 18 January 1918; Brace at Conference with workers' representatives, 17 July 1917.

[26] PRO, PIN 11/1, files relating to 1906 Workmen's Compensation Bill. Engineering Employers' Federation observations, May 1906, p. 9. See Presentation of Mining Association of Great Britain to Herbert Gladstone, p. 16, for Henry Lewis's comments and a note that claims had risen from 26 per 1,000 in 1899 to 54 per 1000 in 1905.

[27] Legge, 'Industrial Diseases', pp. 26–7.

MRC was pressed into fresh investigations of the subject. In particular, the legal battle for compensation drew attention to the role of the expert witness in the court room as the testimony of geologists and engineers proved vital in deciding key cases on appeal. The preparation and delivery of expert accounts also exposed a significant degree of conflict among different groups of medical and scientific experts for resources, professional status, and political influence in the framing and application of rules relating to compensation for silicosis injuries.

Capital, Labour, and the Experts in Silicosis Schemes, 1918–29

The passage of the Workmen's Compensation (Silicosis) Act of 1918 provided the terms under which workers in the 'refractories' industries, which included ganister mining, were given the right to claim for fibrosis of the lungs due to silica dust. The criterion for a claim was not simply the condition of the lungs established by medical examination. The application for a disablement certificate depended on an individual having worked on or near rock which contained at least 80 per cent of pure or 'free' silica.[28] The examination of the worker was undertaken by a local certifying surgeon registered under the Factory Act of 1901, and referred to a Medical Advisory Committee (later Medical Board) and a recommendation made to the Refractories Compensation Board, which was composed of labour representatives as well as the employers who were the shareholders of the Fund.[29] An important feature of the scheme was the introduction of a periodic medical examination with power to suspend workers suffering from tuberculosis as well as from silicosis. Local tuberculosis officers were frequently involved in the examination and early detection of silicosis, although they were criticized in the Home Office for lack of uniform standards and expertise and were largely superseded by specialists after 1925.[30] Compensation could be awarded for partial as well as total disability, providing the applicant could demonstrate that continued work in the industry would lead to a serious deterioration of their silicosis. After amendments in 1925 and the creation of a Medical Board, there was little scope for the employment of medical referees with a specialist knowledge of pulmonary disease, as occurred in many other trades[31] By pooling the risks it was assumed that individual firms would have little incentive to dismiss workers who were found to be suffering from mild respiratory problems, and employees would be willing to submit to periodic examination. All employers in the refractories industries paid a levy of about 6 per cent of wages, reduced to 5 per cent in 1937, to fund the Compensation Fund

[28] PRO, PIN 12/14, memorandum 'Refractories Industries (Silicosis) Scheme', 4 February 1919.

[29] Report of the Departmental Committee on the Medical Arrangements for the Diagnosis of Silicosis (HMSO, 1929), pp. 8–10. Copy in TUC Papers, 292/144.341/3.

[30] PRO, PIN 12/26, Pottery Industry file, E. Field, 29 December 1923, for criticism of the tuberculosis officers for 'serious lack of uniformity in the examinations'.

[31] Meiklejohn, 'Development of Compensation', pp. 201–3; PRO, PIN 12/131, Workmen's Compensation Committee. A 'Report on Specialist Medical Referees for Industrial Diseases', prepared by Kenneth Goadby stated that of 1,972 cases considered by such referees in 1920–35, 927 were allowed, 941 dismissed, and 104 were made a special reference.

Refractories Scheme. By the end of 1946, compensation had been paid for approximately 1,500 death claims and almost 16,000 incapacity cases, leaving the Fund in heavy surplus.[32]

In the decade that followed the passage of the 1918 silicosis legislation, there was very little progress made in extending the model of industrial insurance to other trades where silica presented a serious hazard to the workforce. One of the most notorious clusters of lung disease was to be found among the grinding and cutlery workers of Sheffield whose traditional reliance on sandstone wheels led to the prevalence of 'grinder's rot' and abbreviated lives in the poorly ventilated workshops of the district. It was estimated in an important study by Macklin in 1923 that about 1,500 grinders worked on cutlery or edge tools, with almost 1,000 others in close proximity to the clouds of dust produced by the silica-rich grindstones. The persistence of sub-contracting and 'little masters' in the tenement workshops only deepened the difficulties of regulating an industry where employment arrangements made the enforcement of Workmen's Compensation law ineffective.[33] Replacing sandstone by abrasive wheels was accomplished reasonably quickly in the years before 1926 but organized employers, both in South Yorkshire and the Midlands, remained stubbornly opposed to schemes of compensation insurance. As the trade unions were too weak and divided to lever their employers into action, an exasperated Home Secretary was reduced to issuing threats to impose individual liability on those cutlery firms which employed 'reputable' labour, although his civil servants remained most anxious that the State should not be drawn into assuming responsibility for the administration of a compensation scheme.[34]

The Workmen's Compensation Act of 1925 consolidated the arrangements for the certification of industrial diseases and affirmed the principle that the employment of medical boards composed of specialist staff was preferable to the use of certifying surgeons and medical referees for the certification of disablement. The refusal of the organized cutlery and tool firms to co-operate in establishing a compulsory insurance fund which would finance specialist medical advisers meant that the British government was forced into scheduling the disease and relying on workers to present themselves to the certifying surgeon, imposing liability on the last employer. Periodic examinations were ruled out and only fatal and

[32] PRO, PIN 12/14, Refractories Industries (Silicosis) Scheme, Home Office Memorandum, 4 February 1919; Actuary to E. Field at Ministry of National Insurance, 21 May 1947.

[33] PRO, PIN 12/23, Report by E. L. Macklin on Sheffield grinding trades, 23 August 1923, Draft for Government Actuary on Workmen's Compensation (Silicosis) Committee, 'Scheme for Grinding Metals'.

[34] PRO, PIN 12/23, Joynson Hicks, Home Secretary, noted of the recalcitrant employers on 14 September 1926: 'These people are evidently determined to have their own way & destroy the scheme'. He issued a threat to the Sheffield Light Trades Employers Association. Two Home Office experts with considerable experience in dealing with northern industrialists, E. L. Macklin and Captain Hacking, warned their superior, Delavigne, of the drawbacks in attempting to impose a scheme on local firms with whom they wished to achieve a co-operative relationship. They concluded that 'the Yorkshire temperament being what it is, the effect would be just the opposite…'.

total disablement claims were allowed.[35] It is difficult to avoid the conclusion that the determination of the employers and relative weakness of organized labour in these fragmented trades enabled the industry to stifle the preventive measures as well as restricting compensation claims.

While negotiations with employers in the sandstone quarrying and cutting trades were reasonably successful, serious difficulties again arose when the British government attempted to introduce a silicosis scheme for the pottery industry. Excessive mortality in the pottery trades of Staffordshire had been the source of comment since William Farr's report of 1875, although it was the TUC's call for an investigation of 'Potters' Asthma' in 1923 which eventually led to the important study by Sutherland and Bryson in 1925. More than one quarter of those working with unmixed flint dust were found to be suffering from silicosis, while rather more than one in seven of those working with general earthenware and chinaware were silicotic. About 5,500 employees were at highest risk of exposure but another 18,000 potters worked with mixed dust, and it was this latter group which the employers wished to exclude from the proposed scheme by limiting its terms to those hands who worked in dust containing at least 80 per cent of free silica. After challenging some of the medical research and radiographic techniques used in the investigation of silicosis in the industry, the employers' representatives declined to consider any insurance scheme which included employees outside the highest-risk groups working with flint dust and resigned from the Departmental Committee appointed to consider compensation arrangements before its report was issued.[36] The trade unions agreed with employers that 'skilled potters' with little prospect of employment outside the industry should be permitted to continue working in the first or milder stage of silicosis, rather than the secondary or tertiary stage of the illness.[37]

It was the bitter experience of clashes with employers in the metal grinding and pottery industries which persuaded the Home Office to frame the 'various industries' scheme of 1928, introduced at the beginning of 1929, encompassing pottery workers along with other occupations whose employment exposed them to very high levels of silica dust. The decision to extend compensation rights to miners other than those employed in the ganister, sandstone, and related industries finally allowed some colliery workers to seek redress for silicosis. The activities of the coal mining unions must also be considered as a significant influence in

[35] PRO, PIN 11/14, Asbestos and Silicosis Bill (1930), 'Notes Prepared for Secretary of State Regarding Possible Amendments by Lord Brentford'; letter from Brentford to Russell, 1 May 1930; PRO, PIN 11/14, NCEO deputation to Home Office, 13 March 1930; R. R. Bannatyne note on NCEO membership, 26 June 1930; memorandum of John Law to Field, 20 February 1930. Notes of Law's evidence at Home Office Conference 25 February 1930 on Sheffield trades. These notes provided a résumé of responses in regard to the Bill of 1930, including the important note that in both the metal grinding and the pottery industries it had not been possible 'even after very protracted negotiations, to secure the co-operation of employers in any Scheme based on a trade Compensation Fund and the whole object of the negotiation therefore failed'.

[36] PRO, PIN 12/26, Report of the Departmental Committee on Compensation for Silicosis dealing with the Pottery Industry [Draft], 1928, pp. 13–19.

[37] PRO, PIN 12/26, Draft Report of a Conference between Medical Members of the Silicosis Committee and the Medical Advisers of the Employers and Operatives, 30 September 1927.

the passage of the 1928 legislation. As early as 1923 it was reported to the Mines Department that an employee of Brodsworth Main Colliery in South Yorkshire had been certified as silicotic by a certifying surgeon and confirmed on appeal to a medical referee, although the firm refused compensation on the grounds that the industry was not subject to silicosis legislation.[38] Although the Department claimed a formidable array of scientific and medical expertise on its Advisory Committee on Occupational Diseases in Mines, this was almost completely concerned with metal mining. One of its members, J. S. Haldane, shared with Edgar Collis and others the common view that coal dust represented no serious threat to the lungs. Haldane also believed that silica dust was relatively rare in most coalfields, until he was persuaded by the determined campaigning of the Somerset Miners' Association (SMA) that the dust arising from underground strata produced hazardous dust which seriously affected colliery workers throughout the mining areas.

It was largely the efforts of the SMA and those of the Anthracite Miners' Association of south Wales which persuaded the Miners' Federation of Great Britain (MFGB) to radically reform the model of compensation provisions embodied under section 47 (3) of the 1925 Compensation Act. By 1928, the Federation had drafted, in collaboration with the Labour Party, a Bill which would sweep away the industrial schemes established after 1918 in favour of a central insurance fund against which all workers harmed by dangerous or irritant dusts could claim. Thomas Legge urgently advised the TUC to retain and adapt the industrial schemes rather than demolishing them. He warned that if this were done 'it would break down at once because of the excessive amount of special medical and technical knowledge (radiography) required to diagnose the malady properly which cannot be obtained except through a scheme system'.[39] Legge subsequently stressed the difficulties faced in identifying the point at which the disease began and in establishing the liability of individual firms. He appeared most concerned to persuade trade union leaders that it was the appearance of tuberculosis which rendered silicosis a disabling disease. Only by scheduling 'silicosis accompanied by tuberculosis' under the Compensation legislation would there be a realistic prospect of awards being granted.[40] Heeding Legge's advice to retain the industrial schemes for silicosis, the TUC pressed on with their plans, although even the return of a Labour Government in 1929 did not lead to the significant

[38] PRO, POWE 8/83, correspondence from Brodsworth Main Colliery to J. W. Lane, 2 September 1923, regarding T. Challends.

[39] Bristol University Archives, Somerset Miners' Association Papers [hereafter SMA Papers], Box 6, Haldane to Swift, 24 August 1930. He added that the 'investigation which we [the Health Advisory Board] caused to be made through official sources confirmed your reports.' J. S. Haldane, 'Silicosis and Coal-Mining', *Transactions—Institution of Mining Engineers*, LXXX (1930–1), 415–51, p. 417, is based on this meeting. Miners Federation of Great Britain (MFGB), Annual Conference, 11 July 1932; *Annual Volume of Proceedings for the Year 1932* (London 1933), p. 113, Swift's speech.

[40] TUC Papers, 292/143.82/4, Legge to Smyth, 25 June 1928; 'I put the matter in this way largely to show how practically impossible I consider it to be to schedule the disease *apart from a scheme system*' (original emphasis). See also 292/144.34/1, memorandum of Meeting, Smyth and Legge, 'Words Used in Scheduling Silicosis', 26 June 1928.

improvements in the 1928 Various Industries arrangements which the mining unions had demanded.[41]

In particular, the scheme which came into force in February 1929 did not provide for partial incapacity and did not permit any retrospective claims from miners and others whose symptoms had become apparent before the arrangements came into force, or who had left the industry more than a year previously. The draft that was distributed to the trade unions for comment did not contain a provision which was subsequently introduced at the insistence of the owners; namely that any silicosis claimants were required to demonstrate that they had worked in or near to rock which contained at least 50 per cent of free silica, whatever the condition of their lungs found in clinical or radiological examination. Bannatyne at the Home Office defended his Department from the bitter criticisms of the MFGB when insisting that the 50 per cent rule was added purely for the purpose of excluding the exceptional conditions found in the granite industry. He justified the refusal of partial disability claims for a different reason; namely, that 'the difficulty of diagnosis of the disease in its early stages' entailed special medical arrangements which were still being considered by a Departmental Committee.[42]

The first decade of legislation providing for the diagnosis, treatment, and compensation of silicosis can hardly be seen as a triumph for medical expertise or for progress in the clinical understanding of the disease. The uncertainties over the diagnosis and certification of the illness, even in the limited number of occupations where employees enjoyed compensation rights, remained a cause for concern. The tuberculosis officers and even the certifying surgeons became the target of senior figures at the Home Office as they pressed for the appointment of specialist boards under their direct control.

One context in which the Home Office pressed for the appointment of senior medical experts to certify silicosis cases can be traced to a long-standing struggle by the Factory Department to resist any intrusion by the new Ministry of Health into the field of occupational health and hygiene. Legge and his Home Office colleagues had sought to transfer the responsibilities of the certifying surgeons to its Factory Inspectorate during the First World War, partly to avoid the duties of factory surgeons 'falling into the hands of School Medical Officers', insisting that clinical work should not be directed by mere administrators. He similarly viewed the prospect of Medical Officers of Health gaining influence over industrial hygiene with disdain in 1922–4.[43] While the BMA became sympathetic to the idea of a Department of Occupational Hygiene under the Chief Medical Officer in 1925, the Home Office expressed its clear opposition to such a

[41] TUC Papers, 292/143.82/1, Workmen's Compensation Bill (Draft), 75 (1).

[42] TUC Papers, 292/144.341/1, 'Miners' Federation of Great Britain: Memorandum on Silicosis among Coal Miners' (*c.* 1929), pp. 4–5, Bannatyne letters, 14 December 1928 and 14 February 1929.

[43] Contemporary Medical Archives Centre (CMAC), Wellcome Library, British Medical Association Papers [hereafter BMA Papers], MP 424, c.145, Correspondence HO (1916–39) Box 65, Note of conversation with Dr Legge, *c.* January 1916; Legge memorandum, 18 February 1922; Legge to Cox, 24 March 1924; Cox to Legge, 1 April 1924.

'revolutionary' suggestion.[44] These tensions may have contributed to the reluctance of the Home Office to embrace the suggestion of Dr Coutts at the Ministry of Health in 1923 that tuberculosis specialists in each area should be involved in the diagnosis and X-ray examination of silicosis sufferers alongside senior clinical experts.[45] Although tuberculosis officers possessed the greatest collective experience of pulmonary disease in the industrial population, they were largely excluded from the certification of silicosis sufferers by the medical arrangements made after 1925.

A second feature in the framing of the industrial schemes developed before 1929 that caused widespread resentment among the trade unions was the continued insistence of geological rather than clinical criteria for the eligibility of claims. The original specification of a minimal silica content in the refractories industry became the subject of intense debate in the potteries, where manufacturers insisted that the threshold of 80 per cent should be retained, even though the working environment of the pot bank differed considerably from the refractories and sandstone quarrying trades. The Home Office similarly defended the retention of the 50 per cent rule in regard to Miners' claims, assuring the MFGB that experts in the Mines Department insisted that '*none of the cases of silicosis among coalminers which have been brought to their notice is due to work in stone containing less than 50 per cent free silica, and that they are unaware of any ground for the suggestion that miners will be prejudiced by reason of this limitation.*'[46] The distinctive views of the Mines Department appear to have been influenced by its traditional responsibility for the control of dust underground and the close relationships which had developed between the Mines Inspectors and mining engineers who collaborated in monitoring the impact of mechanized drilling and dust traps, such as that designed by Captain Hay in the 1920s.[47] Leading figures on the Health Advisory Committee of the Mines Department, including Edgar Collis, Kenneth Goadby, and J. S. Haldane, maintained a co-operative relationship with British coal owners and gradually persuaded them and the Mines Department that the appointment of Dr Sydney Fisher as the first Medical Inspector of Mines in 1927 did not represent a threat to their interests.

Fisher arrived at the Mines Department in a period when the Miners' unions had begun a vigorous campaign to persuade the TUC and the Home Office to extend the scope of the Workmen's Compensation legislation of 1925 to include underground workers in collieries. These activities contributed to the reform of the compensation arrangements which was marked by the introduction

[44] BMA Papers, c.145, Box 65, Cox to Home Secretary, 3 June 1925; BMA deputation to Home Office, 2 July 1925. Comments of Delevigne. It appears that Legge was more ambivalent.

[45] PRO, PIN 12/127, F. J. H. Coutts of Ministry of Health to Sir W. Kinnear, 11 October 1923, expressing astonishment that 'the use of x-rays in assistance of diagnosis had been so largely neglected', arguing that tuberculosis as well as silicosis experts should be involved.

[46] TUC Papers, 292/144.341/1, MFGB memorandum, Bannatyne letter 14 February 1929 (original emphasis).

[47] PRO, POWE 8/112, Chief Inspector Reports on the Adoption of Preventive Measures Suggested as a Result of Dr Piron's Enquiry, Parliamentary questions of D. R. Grenfell, 7 July 1925, and of E. Edwards, 9 February 1926.

of a new Various Industries Scheme in 1929, including some employees at coal mines. The next part of the article considers the contemporary debates on the origins and nature of silicosis which followed the introduction of the Various Industries Compensation Scheme.

Scientific Debates on Silicosis and the Struggle for Reform, 1929–39

The revival of debates on the origins, symptoms, and extent of pulmonary disease among the industrial workforce in Britain may be more easily understood in a context within which there emerged an increasing diversity of political allegiances within the scientific community as well as growing demands by organized labour for a broader interpretation of lung disorders. Changes made in arrangements for the certification of silicosis were a response, at least in part, to the activities of a coalition of activists in different regions of Britain rather than merely registering advances in medical understanding and scientific technique. Growing controversy in regard to the lung diseases found among coal miners, who had usually had minimal exposure to silica dust, compelled medical scientists to re-open the debate on the supposedly unique hazard represented by 'free silica'.

We noted earlier that the protests of the Anthracite Miners' Association and the intervention of Shinwell as Mines Minister had prompted the MRC to seriously reconsider the question of Miners' lung diseases in 1930–1. An early peak in the renewed scientific debate on the question arrived with the controversy over the impact of 'serecite' dust in 1933–4. W. R. 'Serecite' Jones argued that the isolation of silica as the toxic agent in lung disease could not explain the prevalence of illness within the anthracite coalfield of south Wales, where serecite could be found. His claims were rejected by J. S. Haldane and T. D. Jones of Cardiff, while the tuberculosis expert, S. Lyle Cummins, and those critical of Haldane's views on bronchitis and tuberculosis, were more sympathetic.[48] The debate revealed a significant divide between the mining engineers and 'practical' scientists aligned with the British Coal Owners' Research Association (BCORA), led by Haldane, and the medical specialists associated with Lyle Cummins and with the MRC, who often expressed suspicion of mining experts such as T. D. Jones.[49] Having advised colliery and chemicals firms on their defence against

[48] W. R. Jones, 'Silicotic Lungs: The Minerals they Contain', *Journal of Hygiene*, 33 (1933), 307–29; and 'Silicosis', *Bulletin of the Institute of Mining and Metallurgy*, nos 352 and 353, January–February (1934), 341–405; *British Medical Journal*, 10 February, p. 254; 3 March, p. 384, 10 March, p. 452, 19 May, 1934, 920–1; T. D. Jones, 'Silicosis in the South Wales Coalfield: part I—Lung Trouble in the Anthracite Collieries', *Proceedings of South Wales Institute of Engineers*, 52 (1936), 19–244.

[49] Haldane, 'Silicosis and Coal-mining', pp. 424–5, for commendations of Haldane as 'a man of sound practical common sense'. Haldane papers, 20514/210, Draft Report for Committee on Control of Atmospheric Conditions in Hot and Deep Mines, December 1934, p. 6, and Haldane Papers 10306, Report of the Director of Research of the Welsh Memorial Hospital, 31 January 1933. CMAC, Hunter Papers, HUN D 1/1, Diary, 1947: 'Charles M. Fletcher... says that T. D. Jones was an unscrupulous fellow. Not only did he insist that the lung diseases of the south Wales mines is bronchitis derived from exposure in the [Spakes]—Spake Jones—but he wished to prejudice the MRC effort. "I've got the best dust lab in the world. Come to me and do all your dust counts

compensation claims, Haldane was increasingly frustrated at the apparent readiness of medical boards appointed under silicosis legislation to grant disablement certificates without distinguishing fibrosis and 'true silicosis'.[50]

By the early 1930s, many physicians in areas such as south Wales were out of sympathy with Haldane's sceptical views on anthracosis and the harmful effects of coal dust. In chairing a conference of tuberculosis officers and general practitioners in Cardiff during the spring of 1934, Haldane was confronted by a number of speakers who stressed the difficult predicament of older miners forced to 'rush about' in output drives.[51] Some were impatient of the protracted debate on the precise pathology of silicosis when they found miners who were unquestionably victims of lung diseases.[52] At this juncture, Haldane and BCORA sought funding from the Department of Scientific and Industrial Research for fresh research on silicosis, including post-mortem and X-ray analysis. While Haldane acknowledged that he lacked expertise in this field, and the MRC similarly recognized the importance of the geological and petrological research that Haldane and others had undertaken, there appears to have been limited collaboration on the subject.[53] In 1936, the MRC finally embarked on the research investigation into the anthracite coalfield of south Wales which led to the celebrated reports published in 1942–3 on pneumoconiosis.

The representations by mine owners and mining unions of the incidence and severity of lung diseases among the workforce were integral to the debate on silicosis at this time. Challenged to explain the concentration of chest and lung complaints among coal workers in southwest Wales, the Amalgamated Anthracite Collieries Limited insisted that a large number of its employees 'have reached a ripe old age and [...] throughout their lives have been engaged in the mining and preparation of Anthracite coal'.[54] The powerful Mining Association of Great Britain (MAGB) also expressed alarm at the revisions of the 1931 Various Industries Scheme which extended compensation rights to all underground

there." Nevertheless he undoubtedly built the mining school in Cardiff from nothing.' T. D. Jones, 'The Organization of Dust Research in South Wales', *Silicosis, Pneumokoniosis and Dust Suppression in Mines* (London, Institution of Mining Engineers, 1947), pp. 138–47; Discussion, p. 142, for Fletcher's criticism of Jones.

50 Haldane Papers, 10306, interview at Llay Main Collieries, with covering letter, 25 June 1931. Correspondence with Reckitts, manufacturers of cleaning abrasives, 25 January 1923, 20 May 1927, 8 October 1932; PRO, POWE 8/181, 'Health Advisory Committee, minutes of the 46 Meeting held at the Mines Department on Wednesday 17 October 1934'.

51 Haldane papers, 10306, typescript of Hotel Metropole meeting, 20 April 1934, and comments of Dr Griffiths.

52 Haldane papers, 10306, Dr Matthews, 'Neath Area: Silicosis and other Dust Diseases', n.d. *c.* 1934.

53 PRO, FD 1/2879, F. E. Smith of DSIR to E. Mellanby, Medical Research Council, 22 January 1934, regarding the application from the BCORA and noting that: 'I rather gather that the Research Association would be glad to know that an authoritative investigation by an impartial body like the Medical Research Council was being conducted on the question of Silicosis'; Conference of interested parties at MRC, 10 May 1934. Middleton represented the Industrial Pulmonary Diseases Committee. Doubts were expressed about the capacity of T. D. Jones to handle research that was intrinsically medical in orientation.

54 PRO, POWE 8/153, Letter to Under-Secretary for Mines, Mines Department from Amalgamated Anthracite Collieries Limited, 26 January 1931.

workers, and more particularly at the suggestion that such rights might be retrospective since hundreds of applications were awaiting a decision by medical referees. Learning that the Home Secretary was convinced that coal miners faced a serious risk of contracting silicosis, the MAGB stressed the limitations of X-ray techniques in providing any conclusive evidence while also insisting that no financial provision had been made for the award of compensation under the relaxed rules of eligibility now proposed. Again, the coal owners were concerned that these rules would be applied to the large number of cases awaiting certification. The Mining Association urged that all mine workers who were liable to dust exposure should be compelled to undertake a medical examination.[55] Owners of metal mines joined colliery masters in opposing the enlargement of compensation provisions when these were proposed in 1933–4, citing Haldane in support of their view that such reforms would 'be putting legislation too far in advance of scientific knowledge and research of the diagnosis of the disease'.[56] Quarry owners similarly complained in later years that older workers were exploiting the silicosis scheme by returning to an industry they had abandoned some years earlier in order to qualify for compensation which they soon claimed against their employers.[57]

The trade unions were equally vocal in expressing concerns about the restrictions placed on their members as they sought compensation for lung disease. The officials of the National Union of General and Municipal Workers (NUGMW), criticized the inconsistency of diagnosis and government policy in regard to iron ore workers.[58] The leading role among the unions was assumed by the South Wales Miners' Federation (SWMF), which had recovered from the disastrous strike of 1926 and the pit closures which followed, to claim over half the region's 140,000 coal miners as members in 1931, including a large proportion of those employed in the anthracite area.[59] The requirement of the 1931 Various Industries Scheme was that claimants should have worked on or near rock containing at least 50 per cent free silica. The unions were alerted to the need for geological experts to assist in the presentation of the contested compensation cases they wished to take to court.[60] This explains the SWMF's decision in

[55] PRO, POWE 8/183, Minute sheet, 29 October 1934; PRO, POWE 8/172, letter to R. R. Bannatyne from Mining Association of Great Britain, 27 June 1934; POWE 8/183, letter to R. R. Bannatyne from W. A. Lee, 28 September 1934, and draft report, 'Silicosis in Coal mines', n.d.

[56] PRO, POWE 8/189, letter to Home Office from R. Lyon Wyllie, West Coast Hematite Iron Ore Proprietors' Association, 10 October 1934. X-ray evidence used on the South African model was also questioned.

[57] PRO, POWE 8/127, 'Extract from Minutes of "The Quarry Managers Journal" of 5 April 1937, the Sandstone Industry Compensation Fund Ltd., fifth annual general meeting, Report of the Committee on Management'.

[58] PRO, POWE 8/161, letter to Secretary of State for Home Affairs from R. Spence, Assistant General Secretary of National Union of General and Municipal Workers, 26 August 1930.

[59] H. Francis and D. Smith, *The Fed. A History of the South Wales Miners in the Twentieth Century* (London, 1980), pp. 113–14, 176. The SWMF had a membership of 75,480 in January 1931.

[60] R. Page Arnot, *The Miners in Crisis and War: A History of the Miners' Federation of Great Britain* (London, 1961), p. 96.

1933 to commission A. H. Cox, Professor of Geology at Cardiff University, to investigate the implementation of the 1931 Regulations.[61]

The 'Fed' subsequently used Cox's research to attack county court decisions which required the plaintiff to demonstrate that the minimum level of silica was present in rock deposits worked. The union claimed that this rule and the onerous legal and Medical Board fees levied on the miners had resulted in at least 70 miners losing their compensation rights, even though a court had accepted that the plaintiffs' silicosis was likely to have been contracted in the course of their employment.[62] Drawing examples from those gathered in south Wales, the MFGB pressed the Home Office to agree to an extension of the 1931 scheme to cover all underground mine workers. They also called for a relaxation of conditions regarding the silica content of mine strata and the requirement that claimants must have been employed for at least three years to qualify for compensation.

By 1934, the colliery owners accepted that the 1931 scheme should be extended, although only to workers who had been in contact with harmful dust, and they opposed any retrospective awards. They insisted on the appointment of their own medical experts while the SWMF resisted such a policy on the ground that owners could afford more expensive and prestigious consultants than the workforce.[63] In autumn 1934, the Home Office appeared to be committed to an extension of the Various Industries Scheme to all underground workers rather than restricting disablement and death payments to those cases known 'from the science' to have arisen from silica rock.[64] It seems clear that the lobbying activities of the TUC and the mining unions in particular had made a significant contribution to the reforms embodied in the Various Industries (Silicosis) Amendment Scheme of 1934, extending compensation rights to all underground workers despite the serious concerns of the colliery owners.[65]

Another avenue of campaigning and conflict which appears to have influenced the progress of legislation and which involved the rigorous scrutiny of scientific evidence was the legal settlement of complex compensation cases. The courts not only exposed the limits of existing scientific knowledge of silicosis but also the fundamental importance of geological rather than pathological proof in such disputes. Different industrial schemes also specified the period within which a worker could claim compensation and the date at which different rules concerning claims were allowed. A. Meiklejohn believed that the controversy

[61] Cox was Professor of Geology from 1918 to 1949 at University College, Cardiff. The SWMF claimed him as one of Britain's leading geologists. *Who Was Who 1961–1970: A Companion to Who's Who Containing the Biographies of Those Who Died During the Decade 1961–70*, VI (London, 1972), p. 250.

[62] PRO, POWE 8/172, 'South Wales Miners' Federation, October 1933, Various Industries (Silicosis) Scheme 1931', Memorandum and Comments.

[63] PRO, POWE 8/183, letter to Home Office from Ebby Edwards, 17 August 1934; PRO, POWE 8/172, letter to Bannatyne from Mining Association of Great Britain, 27 June 1934.

[64] PRO, POWE 8/183, Home Office minute sheet, August 1934, with addition written in hand, 29 October 1934.

[65] PRO, POWE 8/183, 'Workmen's Compensation Acts, 1925 to 1934', 1934.

surrounding a number of highly publicized cases after 1931 contributed to the reform of the Various Industries Scheme in 1934.[66] An examination of cases before the High Court, Court of Appeal, and the House of Lords also underlines the importance of legal defeats as well as victories for employees in the cases which contributed to the movement for an extension of compensation rights of miners during these years.[67]

One of the points contested in cases brought by the unions and employers concerned the apparent removal, under the 1931 scheme, of the requirement (laid out in Section 47) of the 1928 Silicosis Act that any claimant should have worked in rock containing at least 50 per cent free silica. There remained considerable legal debate as to the meaning of this provision. In *Davies* vs. *Oakdale Navigation Collieries*, the County Court found for the employer on the grounds that the plaintiff had not worked after December 1928 in rock containing 50 per cent silica.[68] In another case, a collier who had merely handled rock in coal trucks was awarded compensation, the Master of the Rolls noting at the Appeal Court that the miner had worked faithfully in the pits for 30 years and was 'just the sort of case which one hopes has been provided for by the schemes like the Silicosis Scheme'.[69] A Cumberland coal owner similarly lost an appeal in claiming that a ripper had never worked in sandstone rock.[70]

Courts deciding on the minimum silica content of rock did rely on expert testimony from geologists, as when Dalton Main Collieries successfully refused a miner's claim after courts accepted a geologist's view that the shale in which he had been working since 1928 contained no silica.[71] The Amalgamated Anthracite Collieries in south Wales also succeeded in resisting the claims of two miners after a County Court reaffirmed its view that the geological evidence presented by the company's expert was superior to that offered by the Miners' Federation witness.[72] At the second appeal, Lord Hanworth (Master of the Rolls), acknowledged the limitations imposed under the 1931 scheme, noting that 'a man who is employed in almost every sort of dust' might ultimately suffer from silicosis, although that was not the statutory basis for compensation laid down by Parliament.[73] Hanworth's comments might be read as a sceptical commentary on the limited scientific understanding of the disease, or even an invitation to further legislation, although in practice such cases alerted labour representatives as well

[66] Meiklejohn, 'Development of Compensation', p. 208.

[67] C. R. Epp, 'External Pressure and the Supreme Court's Agenda', in C. W. Clayton and H. Gillman (eds), *Supreme Court Decision Making: New Institutionalist Approaches* (London, 1999), 249–60, p. 256, provides a conceptual framework.

[68] *Butterworth's Workmen's Compensation Cases* (hereafter BWCC), XXV, new series (January to December 1932), 375–7.

[69] BWCC, XXV, new series (January–December 1932), 635–8.

[70] BWCC, XXVI, new series (January–December 1933), 197–213, *Kilbride* vs. *William Harrison Ltd.*

[71] BWCC, XXVII, new series (January–December 1934), 181–9, *Gledhall* vs. *Dalton Main Collieries Ltd.* Testimony of Professor Gilligan.

[72] BWCC, XXVI, new series (January–December 1933), 573–8, *Amalgamated Anthracite Collieries* vs. *Morgan and Hutchins.*

[73] BWCC, XXVII, new series (January–December 1934), 313–37, 329.

TABLE 1. *Silicosis and asbestosis, 1933–37. Examinations in pursuance of applications for death and disablement certificates 1933–1937*

Disablement	Number of workmen examined					Number certified to be suffering from S or A, or S, or A with TB				
Industry or occupation	1933	1934	1935	1936	1937	1933	1934	1935	1936	1937
Refractories industry	4	10	14	10	8	2	3	7	4	1
Sandstone industry	69	53	53	49	35	53	39	41	32	26
Potteries industry	143	105	128	75	89	70	55	66	26	41
Coal mining industry	282	366	492	674	604	199	211	228	319	256
Masons and stone dressers	99	95	73	79	81	72	67	49	52	56
Metal grinding industries	24	14	16	11	10	13	12	13	5	8
Other industries	29	37	51	103	85	20	23	31	59	33
Asbestos industry	16	10	9	3	7	6	7	4	0	3
Death	Number of applications dealt with					Number certified to be suffering from S or A, or S, or A with TB				
Industry or occupation	1933	1934	1935	1936	1937	1933	1934	1935	1936	1937
Refractories industry	9	5	10	5	7	6	4	7	3	6
Sandstone industry	38	36	51	43	24	32	25	43	25	15
Potteries industry	40	36	39	38	48	31	31	32	31	42
Coal mining industry	43	58	69	118	99	31	35	51	77	72
Masons and stone dressers	39	41	35	41	43	31	31	23	31	26
Metal grinding industries	8	12	10	8	6	6	10	8	7	2
Other industries	14	13	12	28	27	12	11	10	23	24
Asbestos industry	3	2	2	1	0	1	2	1	1	0

Note: S = Silicosis, A = Asbestosis, TB = Tuberculosis
Source: PRO, PIN12/67.

as employers to the vital importance of the detailed provisions made under the compensation schemes.[74]

The impact of the 1934 reforms can be gauged in the increased number of claims made for silicosis compensation, particularly in the coal mining industry. Home Office figures suggest that in 1929 a total of 91 disablement and 68 fatal compensation awards were made in the potteries and refractories trades.[75] After that time, colliery employees figure in the statistics, primarily the 'rock men' or rippers engaged in driving roadways through the headings of silica-rich strata found in many mining districts. Returns for the period 1933–7, summarized in Table 1, indicate the contribution that the coal mining workforce made to British fatalities and disablement due to silicosis.[76]

[74] Hanworth was a Conservative MP from 1910 to 1923 before appointment as Master of the Rolls. *Dictionary of National Biography 1931–40* (Oxford, 1949), pp. 709–10.

[75] PRO, PIN 11/14, Notes in regard to 1930 draft legislation, indicating 68 deaths and 91 disabilities in 1929, 21 and 34 respectively in the potteries, 10 and 19 in refractories, and only 11 disability cases (no deaths) in coal mining. 'Notes prepared for Ministers', indicates a total of 442 applications (including 131 deaths) in the Refractories Scheme since 1919.

TABLE 2. *Certificates of death and disablement granted by the silicosis medical board*

Category	1933	1934	1935	1936	1937	1938
South Wales						
Deaths	28	33	46	69	59	51
Total disablement	126	142	141	224	159	242
Suspension	55	50	51	72	85	149
All disablement	181	192	192	296	244	391
Rest of country						
Deaths	3	2	5	8	13	8
Total disablement	10	14	21	19	25	29
Suspension	8	5	15	4	17	15
All disablement	18	19	36	23	42	44

Source: PRO, FD1/2897, 'Pneumoconiosis in Coal Mines'.

It was even more noticeable that the south Wales coal field dominated the certificates granted by the Silicosis Medical Board to British coal miners for disability and death in these years, indicated in Figure 1 and Table 2.

Conclusions

Studies of the compensation legislation which was introduced for the victims of industrial injury have frequently criticized trade unions for their lethargic response to questions of workplace safety as they pursued financial recompense for the victims of accidents and disease. In his important research on the subject, Bartrip emphasizes the positive contributions made by employers as well as civil servants to the promotion of health at work, as an investigation of hazardous conditions frequently resulted in the 'sensible application of appropriate measures'.[77] The pattern of investigation and reform outlined in this article offers a different interpretation of scientific enquiry and policy responses to that provided by scholars such as Bartrip. We share the view expressed by many historians of science that the creation of a medical consensus on diseases such as silicosis was the result of political and cultural as well as technical advances, involving the building of networks of influence as well as credible witnesses in support of fresh paradigms, such as that which resulted in the new orthodoxy on Miners' pneumoconiosis after 1937.[78]

[76] See Bartrip, *Way From Dusty Death*, p. 43. The subsequent discussion of coal mining refers to the 1940s, although Table 2.3 covers 1935–44 and does not include coal mining. It is unclear if refractories are included.

[77] Bartrip, *Workmen's Compensation in the Twentieth Century*, p. 236. See also A. Bale, 'Medicine in the Industrial Battle: Early Workers' Compensation', *Social Science and Medicine*, 28 (1989), 1113–20, pp. 1115–16, for the limited role of physicians in compensation cases. The quotation is from Bartrip, *Way From Dusty Death*, pp. 29–30.

[78] J. Pickstone, 'Objects and Objectives: Notes on the Material Cultures of Medicine', in G. Lawrence (ed.), *Technologies of Modern Medicine* (London, 1993), 13–24; A. M. Weinberg, 'Science and Trans-Science', *Minerva*, X (1972), 209–22, p. 216.

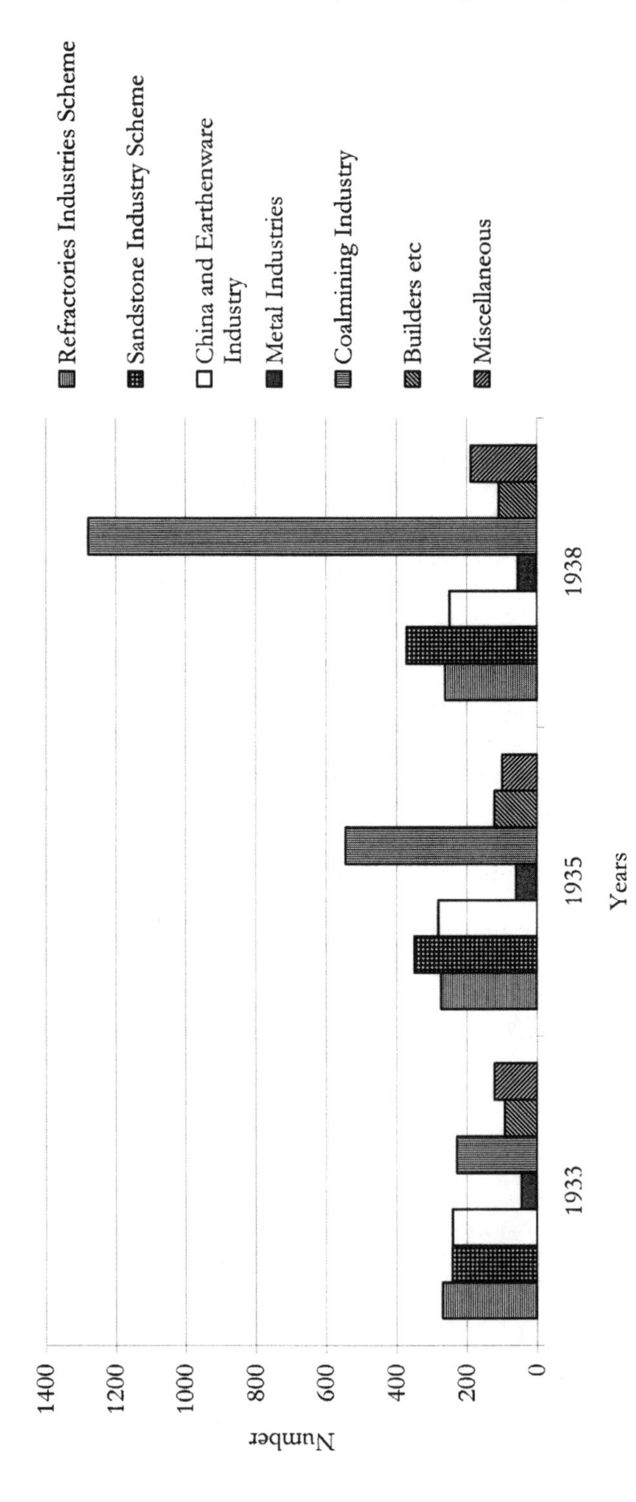

FIG. 1. *Silicosis (non-fatal) Awards 1933–38 under Workmens Compensation Act (Section 47) 1925**
**The terms of the 1925 Act were amended by the Workmen's Compensation Act 1930.*

Source: PRO FD4/243.

In debates on the origins and scale of lung disease among the industrial workforce, organized capital and labour played a prominent part, including the Miners' unions across the British coal fields.[79] The evidence we have surveyed does not support the view that British unions pursued financial awards in preference to campaigns for workplace safety in these years. The reluctance of some groups of workers to present themselves for medical examination and even for compensation appears to have arisen more from a fear of the consequences for their employment than a disregard for their own safety. Such a response becomes more comprehensible where British governments resisted the introduction of compensation schemes for silicosis before 1918, arguing (as did the Samuel Committee of 1907) that the early diagnosis of employees would effectively exclude them from the labour market. Statutory provisions for the compensation of sufferers were not extended to large numbers of employees until 1929 and only the relaxation of eligibility rules in 1934 led to substantial numbers of claims from the largest workforce affected by dust, that of British coal mining.

While the coal owners remained firmly opposed to claims that anthracite and other coal dusts harmed the miners they employed, many firms contributed to research into the prevention of dust at the workplace and fought to influence the research agenda of the Mines Department and the Home Office. Firms in the grinding trades and the potteries were more intransigent, refusing to establish the funds on which the 1919 compensation model depended. These firms rejected Home Office claims that silica dust remained a serious threat in their workshops. Their hostility was less inhibited in part because they did not face the robust unions who negotiated with colliery firms, particularly in south Wales where the anthracite mines yielded the highest concentration of silicosis victims. These unions also figured prominently in the legal battles that exposed forensic evidence regarding silicosis to legal scrutiny in a series of cases after 1929, contributing to the debate on eligibility which resulted in the 1934 reforms.

The most significant and complex relationship discussed in this article is that between medical scientists and the Home Office civil servants responsible for agreeing and framing the details of compensation schemes as well as safety regulations in regard to silicosis during these years. The close ties which often existed between scientists and State employees at the Home Office are apparent where senior inspectors assumed a leading role in medical research as well as the investigation of dangerous occupations. The creation of a powerful orthodoxy on the distinctive hazards presented by silica can be traced to a fairly tight group of Home Office experts on industrial disease, including Legge, Collis, and Middleton as well as scientists such as Haldane. Supported by research undertaken in South Africa, such authorities concentrated on measuring the free silica which pervaded the workplace rather than the much more complex and ambiguous evidence of lung diseases in the larger industrial population. When faced with radical trade union proposals to compensate all workers suffering from the effects of any industrial dust, Legge and his Home Office contemporaries were most reluctant to

[79] Francis and Smith, *The Fed*, p. 439.

abandon the model of silicosis compensation devised in 1918–19. Their conservatism appears to have been sustained by the problems of clear and early diagnosis of respiratory illness caused by the work environment and distinguishing these symptoms from those associated with tuberculosis. Home Office experts were aware that employers and insurance firms would demand indisputable evidence of a link between a specific occupation and the incidence of disease. The isolation of silica as the hazardous agent and the relaxation of qualifying conditions for compensation claims in 1929–34 did not address the toxic affects of coal dust in the anthracite districts, which the MRC finally tackled after 1937, as a result of persistent campaigning by the Miners' unions.

Acknowledgements

The research upon which this article is based was generously funded by the Wellcome Trust. Robert Turner assisted in the collection and collation of original data. Two anonymous referees and the editors of *Social History of Medicine* offered useful comments.

Social History of Medicine Vol. 18 No. 1 © *The Society for the Social History of Medicine 2005, all rights reserved.*
doi:10.1093/sochis/hki002

The Politics of School Sex Education Policy in England and Wales from the 1940s to the 1960s

By JAMES HAMPSHIRE*

SUMMARY. This article explores the political history of school sex education policy in England and Wales. Focusing on the period from the 1940s to the 1960s, it shows how sex education developed as a controversial political issue through an analysis of the differing institutional cultures and agendas of health and education administrators. The article argues that serious consideration of school sex education by central government was first prompted by concern about venereal disease during the Second World War. Thereafter, two groups of actors emerged with conflicting ideas about the role of government in prescribing school sex education. The medical establishment, including the Ministry of Health, was broadly supportive of a national policy, whereas the Department of Education, which had ultimate responsibility for any such policy in schools, sought to avoid decision-making about the issue. The article explores how a public health consensus on sex education developed and then explains why the Department of Education resisted this consensus.

KEYWORDS: sex education, sex, politics, venereal disease, public health, health education.

It is widely observed that sex education is a controversial and divisive issue in British politics, yet little is known about how this came to be. This article explores the politics of school sex education policy in England and Wales from the 1940s to the 1960s, a period which saw the emergence of a policy debate as well as the development of a political conflict that has dogged the subject ever since. Up until the 1940s, the British government was virtually silent on the issue of sex education in schools.[1] It was only during the Second World War, when venereal disease (VD) reached record levels, that school sex education was first seriously considered by central government. As the incidence of VD declined during the 1950s, sex education receded from the official mind, only to return again with redoubled force in the 1960s, when VD was on the increase and a polarized debate about perceived changes in sexual behaviour was under way. During this period, a conflict developed between the major policy actors, based on a tension between public health imperatives and political considerations. From the early 1960s, the medical establishment, which included the Ministry of Health as well as public health authorities and doctors' organizations, made repeated calls for the government to initiate a national policy on school sex education. The Department of Education, which was responsible for policy initiation and implementation, refused to heed these calls because of its concerns about the political implications of legislating on sex education. This conflict over the

*Department of International Relations and Politics, University of Sussex, Falmer, Brighton BN1 9SJ, UK. E-mail: j.a.hampshire@sussex.ac.uk

[1] L. A. Hall refers to a 'traditional silence' on sex education in schools. See L. A. Hall, *Sex, Gender and Social Change in Britain since 1880* (Basingstoke, 2000), p. 148.

desirability of legislation explains why the public health consensus on sex education did not translate into a national policy.

The literature on sex education in post-war Britain has paid scant attention to the history of this conflict.[2] Most academic studies of the politics of sex education in England and Wales have concentrated on the 1980s and 1990s,[3] while broader histories of sex have only briefly touched upon education.[4] This scholarly lacuna perhaps reflects the fact that, up until the late 1960s, school sex education was not the high-profile political issue that it subsequently became. However, during the 1940s and early 1960s, school sex education *was* being debated at Whitehall and by a range of lobby groups, and the contours of later political debate were being staked out. Drawing upon a range of archival materials, most of which have not been analysed before, this article shows that health and education authorities were at loggerheads over school sex education. The focus on official policy, rather than on wider aspects of sex education, allows for a detailed exploration of policy debates and conflicts that have been of long-term importance for school sex education.[5]

The first section of the article explores how sex education in schools emerged as a policy issue at central government level during the Second World War. It was at this stage that the contrast between public health professionals' enthusiasm for sex education and the reluctant approach of the Board of Education took shape. The second section illustrates how a public health consensus on sex education developed in response to the upward trends in VD during the early 1960s. This was part of a wider current of belief in health education and an optimism about the potential of medical science as a whole.[6] Sex education was defined by the medical establishment as a key preventive strategy for VD and it was accorded a central role in the growing field of health education. Influential organizations such as the British Medical Association (hereafter the BMA) began to lobby

[2] Although the vicissitudes of 'medico-moral politics' in general are discussed by F. Mort in his *Dangerous Sexualities: Medico-Moral Politics in England since 1880*, 2nd edn (London, 2000).

[3] For example, M. Durham, *Sex and Politics: The Family and Morality in the Thatcher Years* (Basingstoke, 1991); J. Lewis and T. Knijn, 'The Politics of Sex Education Policy in England and Wales and The Netherlands since the 1980s', *Journal of Social Policy*, 31 (2002), 669–94; P. Meredith, *Sex Education: Political Issues in Britain and Europe* (London, 1989); R. Thomson, 'Unholy Alliances: The Recent Politics of Sex Education', in J. Bristow and A. Wilson (eds), *Activating Theory: Lesbian, Gay and Bisexual Politics* (London, 1993), 219–45; R. Thomson, 'Moral Rhetoric and Public Health Pragmatism: The Recent Politics of Sex Education', *Feminist Review*, 48 (1994), 40–60; idem, 'Prevention, Promotion and Adolescent Sexuality: The Politics of School Sex Education in England and Wales', *Sexual and Marital Therapy*, 9 (1994), 115–26; M. Waites, 'Regulation of Sexuality: Age of Consent, Section 28 and Sex Education', *Parliamentary Affairs*, 54 (2001), 495–508.

[4] The following studies of sex and society all address sex education at various points: L. Bland, *Banishing the Beast: English Feminism and Sexual Morality 1885–1914* (London, 1995); Hall, *Sex, Gender and Social Change*; L. A. Hall and R. Porter, *The Facts of Life: The Creation of Sexual Knowledge in Britain, 1650–1950* (London, 1995); J. Weeks, *Sex, Politics and Society: The Regulation of Sexuality since 1800*, 2nd edn (London, 1989). A brief overview of sex education from the late nineteenth to the late twentieth century is provided by L. A. Hall, 'Sex Education in Britain, 1870–1995', *History Review*, 23 (1995), 47–51.

[5] See Lewis and Knijn, 'The Politics of Sex Education Policy', for a comparison of the adversarial approach in England and Wales with the more consensual approach taken in The Netherlands.

[6] V. Berridge, *Health and Society in Britain since 1939* (Cambridge, 1999), p. 2.

government for a national policy. Although it would be an overstatement to claim that sex education was viewed as a panacea by those engaged in the fight against VD, it was nevertheless seen in unremittingly positive terms and, subsequently, its 'difficult' aspects were overlooked. By the mid-1960s, a public health consensus on sex education, which included the Ministry of Health, was in place.

The third section of the article considers the Department of Education's response to this consensus and illustrates how a combination of political expediency and principle led it to adopt a hands-off approach. Hoping to avoid embroilment in the growing controversy about unmarried pregnancy, abortion, and the sexual behaviour of the young, the Department refused to initiate a national policy and instead issued optional guidance in the form of departmental pamphlets;[7] a strategy which satisfied neither public health lobbyists nor moral traditionalists.

VD and the Development of Sex Education

The first serious investigation into sex education in schools by the British government was prompted by the high incidence of VD during the Second World War, although it is important to note that the association of VD and sex education had a longer history. Sex education had preoccupied nineteenth-century VD campaigners, especially those associated with the social purity movement,[8] and from the 1890s an increasing number of educational publications emerged warning against the dangers of sexual sin.[9] In 1914, VD campaigners formed the National Council for Combatting [sic] Venereal Diseases (NCCVD), which developed propaganda and educational measures.[10] As the First World War unfolded, fears about the effects of VD on the health and fitness of soldiers led to the appointment of a Royal Commission on Venereal Diseases, which reported in 1916 and recommended an immediate improvement in treatment facilities and public education.[11] Notwithstanding these developments, central government did not promote an official programme of school sex education at this time.

During the inter-war period, the need for public education on sex was more widely acknowledged and a diverse range of figures, from the birth control campaigner, Marie Stopes, to the National Vigilance Association, argued the case.

[7] The application of non-decision-making to social policy is discussed by R. Lowe, *The Welfare State in Britain since 1945*, 2nd edn (London, 1999), p. 42. On non-decision-making as a dimension of power, see S. Lukes, *Power: A Radical View* (London, 1974).

[8] J. S. Watson, 'The Role of the Purity Movement in the Development of Sex Education for Young People, 1850–1914' (unpublished Ph.D. thesis, London School of Economics, 1978).

[9] L. A. Hall, *Hidden Anxieties: Male Sexuality, 1900–50* (Cambridge, 1991), pp. 29–32.

[10] L. A. Hall, 'Venereal Diseases and Society in Britain, from the Contagious Diseases Acts to the National Health Service', in R. Davidson and L. A. Hall (eds), *Sex, Sin and Suffering: Venereal Disease and European Society since 1870* (London, 2001), 120–36, p. 125.

[11] D. Evans, 'Tackling the "Hideous Scourge": The Creation of the Venereal Disease Treatment Centres in Early Twentieth-Century Britain', *Social History of Medicine*, 5 (1992), 413–33. Sex and soldiers in the First World War are discussed in L. Sauerteig, 'Sex, Medicine and Morality during the First World War', in R. Cooter, M. Harrison, and S. Sturdy (eds), *War, Medicine and Modernity* (Stroud, 1998), 167–88.

The NCCVD was given a generous block grant by the Ministry of Health to carry out education and propaganda, and a new organization, the Society for the Prevention of Venereal Disease, was formed to promote prophylactic methods.[12] Nevertheless, the inter-war governments continued to show little interest in promoting school sex education.[13]

During the Second World War, health education was viewed as one strand of the total mobilization for war.[14] The campaign against VD was initially co-ordinated by the Ministry of Health alongside the British Social Hygiene Council (formerly the NCCVD) and, after 1942, the Central Council for Health Education (CCHE). Early efforts focused on reaching adults through propaganda in the press, the distribution of pamphlets and posters, and films and lectures advertising local facilities for treatment.[15] In an important Parliamentary debate in December 1942 on the Government's proposal for compulsory treatment of VD, members on both sides of the House argued that the Ministry of Health's efforts on VD education were insufficient.[16] It was suggested that future efforts should begin at school and, in this context, the Board of Education was drawn into the debate. A communication between the Ministry of Health and the Board of Education acknowledged that, although 'the general responsibility in regard to both treatment and education' was for the former department, 'there are aspects of the work which can no doubt best be dealt with by other Departments for particular groups of people', including children in the context of youth clubs and schools.[17] An interdepartmental conference was arranged to discuss these matters. At the meeting there was 'a good deal of encouragement' for the Board to consider issuing information on sexual health to school-leavers and leaders of youth clubs and it was suggested that it undertake a survey of current provision of sex education in schools.[18] The Board somewhat reluctantly acceded to this, concerned as it was with getting involved with what one civil servant later described, with typical Whitehall understatement, as 'a not too easy subject'.[19] The Board commissioned Her Majesty's Inspectorate (HMI) to undertake a survey and resolved to publish a pamphlet on the basis of its findings.

Sex Education in Schools and Youth Organisations (Pamphlet 119), was published in November 1943. It was the first central government publication dedicated to school sex education and was the only such document to contain the phrase

[12] Hall, 'Venereal Diseases and Society in Britain', pp. 127–8.

[13] Hall and Porter, *The Facts of Life*, pp. 238–9. On the lack of sex education in the 'official schooling system' in the inter-war period, see S. Humphries, *A Secret World of Sex. Forbidden Fruit: The British Experience 1900–50* (London, 1988), pp. 48–51. In 1918, M. Stopes published *Married Love* (London, 1918), in which she gave sexual advice to 'average, healthy, mating creatures' (p. xiii).

[14] Berridge, *Health and Society*, pp. 18–22.

[15] See *Hansard [HC]*, 385, col. 508, 19 November 1942.

[16] *Hansard [HC]*, 385, cols 1807–88, 15 December 1942.

[17] The National Archives, Public Record Office (hereafter PRO), ED121/491, J. C. Wrigley to Sir Robert Wood, 5 December 1942.

[18] PRO, ED121/491, Inter-departmental conference on venereal diseases: record of discussion, 12 December 1942.

[19] PRO, ED121/491, Sir Robert Wood to the Secretary of the Board of Education, 24 August 1943.

'sex education' in its title up until the 1980s. The pamphlet consisted of a statement of support for those schools and youth organizations which undertook sex education, but did not offer any concrete guidelines or stipulation that such education should be given. It claimed to provide no more than a 'broad outline of suggested principles in regard to the theory or practice of sex education'.[20] In fact, even this was rather lacking. Notwithstanding its positive tone, the pamphlet was much more of a review of existing practice than a handbook of recommendations. The findings of the HMI survey had suggested that in elementary and secondary schools provision was patchy and, in perhaps one-third of the country, 'practically nothing' whatsoever was done. Even in the schools that made a 'serious attempt', the content of sex education was often limited and was delivered in an informal manner. The Board made clear that it considered 'prior responsibility' for sex education lay with parents, but given that 'a substantial proportion' were failing in this task, schools could 'undertake the very important task of making good the inadequate and distorted knowledge possessed by many children'.[21] The Board would not, however, prescribe sex education classes.

The Board's approach was premised on the idea that sex education was at least partly a private matter, and government should approach it with caution, if at all. Hence the Board's tentative assurance of 'warm support and encouragement' to those schools and youth organizations 'who are giving serious attention to this subject', combined with a conclusion which stopped short of recommending any particular approach. With Pamphlet 119, the Board of Education sought to placate those who believed sex education was a necessary part of the struggle against VD, without recommending a national school sex education policy. This marked the beginning of a strategy of non-decision-making which would continue for the next 40 years.[22]

In the absence of an active education department, the provision of sex education was left up to the initiatives of individual schools with support from voluntary organizations. The two most important groups in this regard were the CCHE and the National Marriage Guidance Council (MGC).[23] Evidence from the CCHE illustrates how, even at this early stage, a conflict between public health professionals and educationalists was emerging. The CCHE was a quasi-autonomous organization, funded largely by voluntary contributions from local authorities (although it did receive a small grant from central government between 1942 and 1946) and its membership was largely made up of doctors. Its influential Education Officer, Cyril Bibby, who developed his interest in the use of sex education as a means of tackling VD whilst he was at the British Social Hygiene Council, noted that the CCHE was dominated by doctors, and

[20] *Sex Education in Schools and Youth Organisations*, Pamphlet No. 119 (London, 1943), Para. 10.

[21] Ibid., Para. 43.

[22] Through administrative reforms, the name of the central government department responsible for education policy changed twice during the period covered by this article: The Board of Education (to 1944), the Ministry of Education and Science (1944–64), and the Department of Education and Science (DES) (April 1964–). When the chronological context is clear, the appropriate name is used. At other times, the Department of Education is used as a generic shorthand.

[23] The Family Planning Association only became involved in school sex education in the 1970s.

that professional educators were poorly represented.[24] As a more recent commentator has summarized the situation: 'the professions of medicine and education never articulated their alliance at that time in any formal way.'[25] The medical bias of the CCHE was compounded by the lack of any official link with schools or schools' organizations, so that although it offered training opportunities to teachers and was sometimes invited into schools, it was not able to make significant inroads into the realm of education to communicate a thorough or consistent message.

Nevertheless, the Council set out to promote health education by producing and distributing pamphlets and other teaching materials,[26] and by giving lectures in schools and youth clubs, as well as to adults in factories and the armed forces.[27] During the war, it became particularly concerned with 'the scope of propaganda on Venereal Diseases and its integration with general health teaching'.[28] In 1943, adolescence and VD were identified as its first and third priorities for film subjects.[29] According to Bibby, by this time, the CCHE had 'got a very good scheme of sex education going, dealing with the psychology, the sociology, the ethics and so on and so forth'.[30] Despite his positive evaluation of these years, however, he admitted that the CCHE was not entirely successful in linking its sex education message to VD: 'We always tried to do what we could, but I don't think we, in connection with venereal disease ... really managed to get across to people ... any overall consideration of sexual behaviour.'[31] What was most striking, he claimed, was that 'large numbers' of teachers, social workers, and youth leaders thought:

> something serious should be done about sex education, but [they] were frightened by two things. First, as long as the Ministry [of Education] and the teachers' organisations and so on were opposed to it, they were afraid they wouldn't get any backing if they ran into trouble, and secondly, they didn't know how to set about it.[32]

Bibby's contention that large numbers of teachers supported the principle of sex education was borne out by Mass Observation's 1949 'Little Kinsey' report, which found that 99 per cent of teachers (and 95 per cent of doctors) were in favour.[33]

[24] Contemporary Medical Archives Centre, Wellcome Library for the History and Understanding of Medicine, London (hereafter CMAC), GC/196, Interview with C. Bibby conducted by G. M. Blythe, 23 August 1981, p. 4.

[25] I. Sutherland, *Health Education: Half a Policy. The Rise and Fall of the Health Education Council* (Cambridge, 1987), p. 16.

[26] The pamphlets published by the CCHE included guidance for teachers (*Health Education in the School*), for parents (*What Shall I Tell My Child?*), and for young people (*From Boyhood to Manhood, Manhood: An Explanation of Sex for Young Boys, The Approach to Womanhood*, and *Yourself and Your Body: A Booklet for Girls*). Copies of all of these pamphlets are contained in PRO, ED121/491.

[27] See CMAC, SA/FPA 661 and NK 234, C. Bibby, 'Sex Education: Aims, Possibilities and Plans', *Nature*, 6 October 1945, 413; 13 October 1945, 438.

[28] PRO, MH82/8, Minutes of the Executive Committee of the CCHE, 29 June 1942. Resolution 16 (a).

[29] Ibid., 8 April 1943. Resolution 101 (b). The second priority was 'cleanliness and good habits in children'.

[30] CMAC, GC/196, Interview with Bibby, p. 7.

[31] Ibid., p. 12.

[32] Ibid., p. 7.

Despite the positive noises made in the Board of Education's Pamphlet 119, Bibby considered the government, especially the Board, to have been obstructive. He complained that they 'wouldn't back up any teacher who did anything in the way of sex education in schools. The National Union of Teachers and the National Association of Teachers were opposed to it'. Indeed, evidence from the Ministry of Health files at The National Archives indicates that on at least one occasion the Board of Education took exception to a health education booklet produced by the CCHE for children.[34] Even if the Ministry of Education and teachers' organizations became 'slightly favourable' in the years immediately after the war, there remained a disjunction between the level of opposition at the centre and the support of both doctors and teachers at the local level.[35]

During the early 1950s, political interest in sex education diminished as the incidence of VD declined.[36] Looking back in 1964, the Chief Medical Officer (hereafter the CMO) lamented that the decline in venereal infections during the early 1950s also led to a loss of interest by the medical profession.[37] As just one measure of the subject's waning political significance, it is notable that between 1950 and 1960 there was not a single question about sex education in Parliament, compared with six such questions in the 1940s and 17 in the 1960s.

The Public Health Consensus on Sex Education

From the late 1950s to the early 1960s, a consensus developed among doctors and public health organizations that sex education in schools was a necessary part of any solution to the growing problem of VD. As a result, the conflict between these groups and the Department of Education intensified. This section explains the development of a public health consensus in favour of sex education in schools, while the next section explores why the Department of Education (DES) resisted it.

From the late 1950s, a new enthusiasm for health education spread through the medical profession. In their history of public health, Walter Holland and Susie Stewart point out how the concept of public health evolved during the twentieth century from its early focus on rectifying conditions that caused infectious diseases to attempts at changing individual behaviour.[38] Howard Leichter locates this shift in the period from the mid-1950s to the 1970s and describes it as 'the second public health revolution'.[39] Certainly, by the 1960s the success of environmental campaigns (for example, the campaign for the Clean Air Act of 1956) led to the

[33] L. Stanley, *Sex Surveyed, 1949–94: From Mass Observation's 'Little Kinsey' to the National Survey and the Hite Reports* (London, 1995), p. 86.

[34] See PRO, MH82/8, Minutes of the Executive Committee of the CCHE, 17 September 1942. Report of the Film and Publications Sub-Committee.

[35] CMAC, GC/196, Interview with Bibby, pp. 5–6.

[36] See Hall, 'Venereal Diseases and Society in Britain', p. 132.

[37] *On the State of the Public Health: The Annual Report of the Chief Medical Officer of the Ministry of Health for the Year 1964* (London, 1965), p. 73.

[38] W. Holland and S. Stewart, *Public Health: The Vision and the Challenge* (London, 1998), p. viii.

[39] H. A. Leichter, *Free to Be Foolish: Politics and Health Promotion in the United States and Great Britain* (Princeton, NJ, 1991), p. 68.

belief that environmental problems had been largely addressed, and 'health education rather than treatment became the major focus of policy'.[40] The two paradigm cases were the campaigns against smoking and VD.[41] Both smoking and VD threatened to undermine the rather complacent 'grand narratives of progress' characteristic of early histories of public health, and tackling them required new strategies aimed at changing the behaviour of individuals.[42] With respect to VD, the Ministry of Health issued a circular in 1959 stating that 'publicity and other established means of health education have a valuable part to play in making generally known the increased incidence of venereal disease'.[43] Both the smoking and VD campaigns emphasized personal responsibility for risk evaluation, which entailed knowledge and therefore education.

Beginning in 1956, the British Cooperative Clinical Group's studies of VD, reported in the *British Journal of Venereal Disease*, showed a steady increase after a decade of decline.[44] In 1959, the CMO for the Ministry of Health reported that various factors explained the upward trends, but noted that 'Medical Officers of Health, doctors at clinics for venereal diseases, social workers and others are especially anxious about sexual promiscuity among young people'. He blamed the 'unsatisfactory home life' of many young people and claimed that the country faced a 'social sickness of which venereal disease is only one symptom'. In a gloomy assessment, the CMO was initially doubtful whether educational measures were sufficient to address this 'because moral standards are based upon stable family life and knowledge does not of itself bring virtue'. He wondered whether society's 'roots in family life may not be suffering from decay'.[45] Subsequent reports were more sanguine about the use of public education to 'improve the sexual habits of society', but they still did not propose sex education in schools.[46] In 1965, however, the CMO came round to the idea that 'instruction of older schoolchildren' was an important part of the fight against VD. In a revealing passage he remarked that 'obtain[ing] full co-operation in this matter is not easy because there persists in the minds of most older people . . . a distaste for discussion of this subject. . . . In some quarters there is still a conspiracy of silence.'[47]

[40] Berridge, *Health and Society*, p. 50.

[41] On smoking, see V. Berridge, 'Science and Policy: The Case of Post-war Smoking Policy', in S. Lock, L. A. Reynolds, and E. M. Tansey (eds), *Ashes to Ashes: The History of Smoking and Health* (Amsterdam, 1998), 143–63.

[42] On the role of such narratives in the historiography of public health, see D. Porter, *Health, Civilization and the State: A History of Public Health from Ancient to Modern Times* (London, 1999), pp. 1–4.

[43] PRO, MH151/76, Circular 6/59, 27 April 1959.

[44] *British Journal of Venereal Disease*, 32 (1956), 21–6; 36 (1960), 233–40; 37 (1961), 216–32; 38 (1962), 1–8; 39 (1963), 1–14. This article focuses on England and Wales. For the history of VD in Scotland, see R. Davidson and G. Davis, '"This Thorniest of Problems": School Sex Education Policy in Scotland 1939–80', *Scottish Historical Review* (forthcoming).

[45] *Report of the Ministry of Health for the Year 1959 Part II: On the State of the Public Health* (London, 1960), pp. 70, 71.

[46] *Report of the Ministry of Health for the Year 1960 Part II: On the State of the Public Health* (London, 1961), p. 61. See also HMSO, *On the State of the Public Health: The Annual Report of the Chief Medical Officer of the Ministry of Health for the Year 1963* (London, 1964), p. 70.

[47] *On the State of the Public Health: The Annual Report of the Chief Medical Officer of the Ministry of Health for the Year 1965* (London, 1965), pp. 82–3.

By 1966, the CMO reported that there was 'considerable scope for improvement' in the matter of 'educating and instructing the public, and especially young people, in the delicate matter of sexual relationships'.[48]

This shift in the CMO's assessment came after several years of lobbying from influential actors in the field of health policy. In particular, the decision of the BMA to back a national policy on school sex education was essential to the generation of a public health consensus. From the late 1950s onwards, concern about VD rates drove the BMA to become ever more vocal on school sex education. Its Subject of the Year for 1959–60 was 'The Medical and Social Problems of Adolescence', and over the course of that year doctors from local divisions of the BMA were canvassed for their opinions on medical subjects associated with young people. The end of year report, *The Adolescent*, discussed the alleged trend towards promiscuity and reported that doctors in all of the divisions approved of some form of sex education, although there were differences about the emphasis of responsibility between parents and teachers.[49] Picking up on themes that had been identified as particularly important during 1959–60, and reflecting the growing interest in the subject, the next Subject of the Year was 'Health Education'. That year's report stated that there was now unanimous agreement among the local divisions on the need for improved school sex education. Although 'the prime responsibility for sex education [lay] with parents', given the widespread failure to meet this responsibility, it argued that schools must play a role. The report recommended that all student teachers be given training in sex education and insisted that, at the very least, 'boys and girls should know of the danger to health of sexual promiscuity'.[50]

This position was not yet official BMA policy, but it became so over the next two years as anxiety about VD grew. During 1960, the BMA's Venerologists' Group Committee received evidence from treatment clinics corroborating the CMO's report for 1959 that VD had increased. Following this, the BMA Council established a committee to investigate and consider practical measures for combating VD by co-ordinating the activities of various groups and influencing public opinion. Chaired by J. R. Nicholson-Lailey, a consultant gynaecologist, the committee found that, although syphilis had declined up until 1958, there had been an upturn in cases since then. The increase in gonorrhoea was even more troubling: the number of new cases at clinics for 1959 stood at 31,344 compared with a figure of 18,064 for 1951. The committee argued that there was a threefold explanation for these increases: 'the influx of coloured immigrants'; 'male homosexuals'; and 'the increase of promiscuity among young people'.[51] It considered the last factor especially disturbing 'particularly as the age of contraction appeared to be lowering'. The committee was initially pessimistic that

[48] *On the State of the Public Health: The Annual Report of the Chief Medical Officer of the Ministry of Health for the Year 1966* (London, 1967), p. 79.

[49] British Medical Association Archive, London (hereafter BMA), B/55/8/13, *The Adolescent* (London, 1961), Recommendation 6.

[50] BMA, 20/108/9, *Health Education*, (London, 1962), p. 21, and Recommendations 19 and 20.

[51] Similar causes were identified in the *British Journal of Venereal Diseases*, 32 (1956), p. 15.

educational measures could be more than contributory, but over the course of its investigations it came to identify schools and youth clubs as important targets for education 'to alter the present conception of sexual relations in the mind of modern youth'.[52]

The results of the committee's investigations were published in March 1964 as a BMA Report entitled *Venereal Disease and Young People*. It made several recommendations on sex education.[53] The first main recommendation was that LEAs, school governors, and individual teachers should co-operate to work out programmes for instructing teachers, student teachers, and parents in 'methods of giving the necessary knowledge about sex, within the broader educational concept already outlined'; secondly, it argued 'that the responsible authorities in the health and education fields be encouraged to make more use of trained lecturers on health and family life education in schools'; thirdly, suitable handbooks for parents and teachers should be produced 'giving information about sex in relation to marriage, the home, the family and social responsibility in the community as a whole'; fourthly, advisors on sex-related issues should be employed at colleges and universities; and, finally, greater emphasis should be given to helping with 'family life' issues, such as marital or adolescent difficulties, in the education of family doctors.

Following the publication of the report, which received a large amount of press attention, the BMA organized a Conference on 'Venereal Disease Among Young People' in November 1964. The conference was attended by doctors, health professionals, church representatives, and some teachers, although the President of the Metropolitan Catholic Teachers' Association complained that it was 'devoid of teachers'.[54] It was widely agreed that the current provision of sex education was unsatisfactory. Too few schools offered adequate teaching in this area, such teaching as was offered was of poor quality, and most of the available sex education books were 'out of touch with modern thinking'.[55] The conference resolved that a 'comprehensive national policy' on sex education was needed if VD was to be tackled, and it recommended that sex education should become an integral part of the school syllabus.[56] Thus the single most influential pressure group in the medical field, with a monopoly of representation and expertise, was now in favour of a national policy on school sex education.

Similar conclusions were also reached by the Cohen Report on *Health Education* which was published in the same year. Most well known for its recommendation that a new central authority was needed for health education, the report argued that sex education, including teaching about 'human relationships', was one area in which more education was 'much needed'. Alongside 'the ill effects

[52] BMA, B324/1/1, Agenda of the Nicholson-Lailey Committee, 18 May 1961.

[53] BMA, B324/2/1, *Venereal Disease and Young People: A Report by a Committee of the British Medical Association on the Problem of Venereal Disease, Particularly Among Young People* (London, 1964). The report's key findings were summarized in a pamphlet intended for a lay audience: *VD: The Facts*.

[54] BMA, B324/1/4, Copy of Agenda, 1 December 1964.

[55] BMA, B324/1/4, Report to Conference from Dr Doris Odlum, 7 November 1964.

[56] See 'Sex Education Urged as Part of School Syllabus', *Guardian*, 9 November 1964.

of smoking', ignorance about sex was seen to constitute a major health problem. Particular attention needed to be paid in schools to education about the relationships of the sexes in all its human and social implications, including future responsibilities as parent.[57] Sex education, the report claimed, 'might help to reduce unwanted pregnancies and venereal disease in teenagers'.[58] Significantly, the DES took issue with several of the report's conclusions, especially on sex education. An internal memorandum insisted that the Department's current pamphlets were sufficient and indicated its desire to avoid controversy. The suggestion that health education should have a specific role in the school timetable was seen as 'a very controversial one'.[59]

The now substantial interest in health education within the medical profession was finally given official recognition with the establishment of the Health Education Council (HEC) in 1968. Established by the Ministry of Health to plan and promote national programmes of health education, and to assist in the development of local programmes in co-operation with local authorities and professional organizations, the HEC would prove to be another influential advocate of school sex education. Given that its 15 members were drawn almost entirely from the fields of medicine and public health (only one member was nominated by the Secretary of State for Education), this was hardly surprising.[60] The HEC took over the health education activities of the Ministry of Health and superseded the CCHE. In the press release announcing its launch, Kenneth Robinson, the Minister of Health, quoted the World Health Organization's aims for health education: 'to equip people with the skills, knowledge and attitudes to enable them to solve their own health problems'.[61] In the area of sex education this readily translated into an approach that stressed individual choice, which was anathema to moral authoritarians and discomforting for the DES. Particularly under its second chairperson, Lady Alma Birk, a Labour Life Peer and Vice-President of the Council for Children's Welfare, the HEC placed a strong emphasis on sex education and embarked on a series of high profile campaigns.[62]

In addition to providing materials and lecturers for schools, and organizing conferences, the HEC adopted an active lobbying role.[63] Shortly after her appointment, Birk told the *Medical News Tribune* that she wanted sex education accepted in the school curriculum and help for student teachers on how to conduct sex education lessons: 'We're awfully inhibited still as a society, about

[57] *Health Education. Report of a Joint Committee of the Central and Scottish Health Services Council* (London, 1964), Recommendation 43. See also Para. 4.

[58] Ibid., Para. 263; cf. Paras 47 and 4.

[59] PRO, ED50/860, Harper to Browne, 18 December 1964.

[60] See PRO, MH154/476, Kenneth Robinson to Dr Elfed Thomas, 18 January 1968.

[61] PRO, MH154/476, Ministry of Health Press Service, 'New Health Education Council Inaugurated. Minister Speaks of "Exciting Venture"', 2 January 1968.

[62] Baroness Serota was the first chairperson of the HEC. She left in May 1968 to take up a ministerial appointment, and was replaced by Lady Birk in 1969. Birk was an associate editor of *Nova*, and shortly after her appointment she wrote that 'the Health Education Council has made sex education one of its priorities', *Nova*, December 1969.

[63] See the letter by Birk to *The Times*, 25 July 1969 in CMAC, SA/FPA 594 B10/49.

many things, sex and sex education particularly, and this is why we've no coherent or consistent policy.'[64] Birk placed a new emphasis on the personal and social relationships aspects of sex education and stressed the importance of individual choice, saying that 'few boys and girls leave school having had sex education set in the context of living and human relationships. They must know what the choices in sexual behaviour are.'[65]

The specialist medical press and other groups with an interest in public health also coalesced in support of sex education in schools. For example, a leading article in *The Lancet* on VD and young people recommended that more extensive use should be made of lecturers and leaflets to educate school children on sexual health.[66] Meanwhile, in 1965, the Royal College of Midwives published a report on 'Preparation for Parenthood' in which it argued that 'there [was] still a need for considerable extension of this [sex education] teaching'. It recommended that each local authority area should have special teachers who would visit schools, colleges, youth clubs, and other groups of young people to teach sex education.[67] In every medical and public health journal from this period one can find similar assessments. *Family Doctor* insisted that 'there can be no doubt of the importance of providing children and young people with a proper knowledge of the facts of the sex relationship and of its place in their lives'.[68] *Pulse* reported on a lecture by the Liverpool gynaecologist, H. H. Francis, given to the Royal Society of Medicine, in which he claimed that 'we cannot give teenagers too much sex advice'.[69] And in 1969, *Pulse* published an article entitled 'Sex Education must be given in School'. It claimed that its own recent enquiry on the implications of the 1967 Abortion Act showed that about 70 per cent of all the doctors who replied had asked for improved family planning services, contraceptive advice freely given in the community, and a concerted programme of sex education in schools.[70]

Thus, between the late 1950s and mid-1960s, a consensus developed among the medical community that better sex education in schools was required in the fight against VD. This consensus formed because doctors and public health professionals agreed that a national programme of school sex education was a necessary, although not sufficient, condition to secure the goal of arresting or even reversing VD rates. Support for sex education from a public health perspective was therefore uncontroversial. As far as the Ministry of Health, the BMA, the CCHE and later the HEC were concerned, there was a clear argument for a national policy on public health grounds.

[64] *Medical News Tribune*, 5 December 1969.

[65] CMAC, SA/FPA 594 B10/49, clipping from *FPA News*, April 1969. Around this time the phrase 'personal relationships' began to emerge in the sex education lexicon. For example, see K. Falk, 'Education for Personal Relationships', *Pulse*, 15 November 1969, pp. 14–15.

[66] *The Lancet*, 14 March 1964, p. 596.

[67] Royal College of Midwives, *Preparation for Parenthood* (London, 1965), p. 15.

[68] *Family Doctor*, May 1962, p. 10.

[69] *Pulse*, 16 November 1968, p. 9.

[70] *Pulse*, 16 August 1969, p. 4. The survey was reported in the issue of 24 May 1969, p. 1.

Resisting the Public Health Consensus: The Department of Education's Non-decision-making Strategy

At the BMA conference on VD in November 1964, the Government's representative, Lord Stonham, Under-Secretary of State for the Home Office, put the argument against a national policy on school sex education. In his introductory speech, Lord Stonham spelt out the reasons why the Government was reluctant to act too hastily on the health establishment's demands:

> My presence here to open this conference should not lead anyone to think that there is any easy solution to the problems of venereal disease or sexual promiscuity to be found by looking to the Government for a lead. In modern times, with the increasing complexity of society, Governments of all political shades have found it necessary to intervene in many fields of activity in society. I do not regret that and, speaking as a politician, I am sure the State will have to intervene from time to time in the interests of the well-being of society. But, in a society which is free and democratic, we must put a limit to this process and in a matter so intensely personal as sexual relationships between individuals, it would be neither right or profitable for the Government to play a leading role.[71]

Despite the consensus among the health establishment that school sex education was an essential weapon in the fight against VD, the DES resisted demands for a national policy. As one civil servant put it, 'we do not prescribe what should be taught in schools nor how it should be taught; this is a matter for teachers'.[72] Although the DES paid lip service to the concerns over VD, they were simply not willing to take direct control of the issue through legislation, and insisted that the departmental pamphlets, combined with provision from the HEC and Family Planning Association (FPA), were sufficient. To go beyond this would be an illegitimate extension of state activity:

> In England and Wales the school curriculum and the way in which any subject in it is taught are matters for the local education authorities and teachers. This applies to health education in schools, no less than to any other subject. Advice on sex education is, however, contained in the Ministry of Education's publication 'Health Education', a handbook of suggestions for the consideration of teachers and others concerned with the health and education of children and young people.[73]

Just as the Board of Education had done in 1943, during the 1960s the DES pursued a policy of non-decision-making. It stonewalled in order to avoid taking overt and controversial decisions.[74] There were three main reasons for this: first, a pragmatic concern within the DES about the controversy that it believed involvement in sex education would entail; secondly, the opposition of prominent individuals, not least the Secretary of State for Education, Edward Boyle, who was personally committed to keeping out of 'moral' issues; and thirdly, opposition from the National Union of Teachers (NUT) to central government direction on curriculum matters. Underlying each of these reasons, to a

[71] PRO, ED50/862, Speech by Lord Stonham to the BMA Conference on Venereal Disease and Young People, November 1964.

[72] PRO, ED50/862, R. Prentice to Revd A. D. Adeney, 5 January 1965.

[73] PRO, ED50/862, F. W. Beale to R. Hickey, 17 July 1964.

[74] Lowe, *The Welfare State in Britain*, p. 42.

greater or lesser degree, was a view of sex education as a morally loaded issue. Any policy would raise awkward and possibly divisive questions about the State's role in a sphere that had traditionally been seen as private and the domain of parental responsibility.

A deep-seated reluctance to become embroiled in a controversial area such as sex education had always played a role in the Department's thinking, but in the climate of the 1960s, as fractious debates over 'permissiveness' were unfolding,[75] the pragmatic case for taking a back seat appeared overwhelming. The public debate on the causes and consequences of permissiveness rendered sex education a potentially explosive issue. Especially towards the end of the decade, sex education became caught up in controversial debates about unmarried pregnancy, abortion, and the sexual behaviour of young people.

Although claims that a rapid shift in sexual behaviour and attitudes was underway were challenged at the time, the moral panic that surrounded these claims was pervasive. In his 1965 Study, *The Sexual Behaviour of Young People*, Michael Schofield argued that fears over alleged promiscuity among young people were ill-founded. Similarly, G. M. Carstairs, a Professor of Psychological Medicine, warned in one of his 1962 Reith Lectures that 'we may be quite mistaken in our alarm—at times mounting almost to panic—over young people's sexual experimentation'.[76] But overwhelmingly adverse, and often hostile, reactions in the popular press drowned out such voices. In addition, there were indications that the Church, which had been broadly supportive of sex education up until this point, was beginning to express doubts, although more about the content rather than the principle of such teaching. The Church of England's Board of Education published a 32-page booklet on *Sex Education in Schools*, which stressed that, although schools should accept some responsibility for sex education, it remained primarily a role for parents. Moreover, they argued that it should not appear in the school timetable, since it was not a 'subject' in the normal sense of that term.[77]

The DES's pragmatic concern to avoid political controversy was reinforced by an ideological commitment to limit government intervention in an area perceived to be the primary responsibility of parents. Many within the department believed that sex education could not legitimately be directed from Whitehall, as became apparent through an incident in 1963, which engendered a major public debate on sex education. In July 1963, Dr Peter Henderson, the Principal Medical Officer at the Ministry of Education, gave a speech to a conference of teachers in Cambridge in which he commented that: 'I don't think it is wrong if a young man and a young woman who are in love and who intend to get married but who are put off marriage, perhaps for economic reasons, have sexual intercourse before marriage.'[78] This remark set off a minor public

[75] For an overview, see J. Lewis, *Women in Britain since 1945* (Oxford, 1992), pp. 40–64.

[76] M. Schofield, *The Sexual Behaviour of Young People* (London, 1965); G. M. Carstairs, *This Island Now* (Harmondsworth, 1964), p. 49.

[77] *The Times*, 2 October 1964.

[78] PRO, ED50/862, clipping from the *Daily Express*, 30 July 1963.

scandal as newspapers berated Henderson for his remarks.[79] Within a day of the speech, Sir Edward Boyle was under pressure to reprimand or even dismiss his medical officer. A group of MPs tabled a motion calling on Boyle to repudiate Dr Henderson's views, but he refused to do so and gave a written answer stating that Henderson was expressing a personal opinion.[80] Boyle was saved a further grilling by the summer recess, but the so-called 'chastity storm' continued in the popular press, and indeed expanded to include diatribes against educationalists and sex education in general. In August, a civil servant minuted Boyle to warn that 'the argument could . . . get very wide'. The *Sunday Telegraph* conducted a survey to ask: 'Do you agree with what Dr Henderson has said, or do you disagree?'. It reported that 66 per cent disagreed, 17 per cent agreed, and 17 per cent did not know.[81] In the face of this, Boyle made some concessions, acknowledging that Dr Henderson's remarks may have 'created an unfortunate impression' but, crucially, he insisted that it was not the role of the Ministry of Education to 'lay down the law on this subject'.[82] In response to growing calls for him to make a 'moral' statement on the content of sex and health education, Boyle insisted that 'teachers must make their own decisions on sex lessons' and issued a press notice:

> The position has always been and remains, that under our system of education, the teaching of moral values is the province of the teachers inside the schools, just as inside the home it is the province of the parents. The Ministry does not lay down what teachers should teach on these matters, and it would be wrong for me as Minister to seek to make an authoritative statement or to try to impose a view on the schools.[83]

In a reply to the Archbishop Lord Fisher of Lambeth, who had called upon the Secretary of State to make 'a simple positive statement on morals', Boyle responded: 'I deeply respect your motive but I cannot help thinking that if Government began to interfere thus in the private life of the individual the departure made from the practice of Government as we know it could go very far.'[84] Roy Nash, Education Correspondent for the *Daily Mail*, explained that Boyle was reluctant to speak out for fear that the row could easily 'develop into a major issue about control over what is taught in Britain's schools'. Nash contended that the Minister wished to avoid this at all costs, as 'his private view . . . is that, if he took any public stand either for or against Dr. Henderson, he would open the way to central direction about what teachers might teach on a variety of topics'.[85] Fortunately for Boyle, by the time Parliament reopened in October the controversy had blown over.

The combination of pragmatism and principle which underpinned the DES's position was also apparent in the evasive responses given by ministers to

[79] See *Evening Standard*, 30 July 1963; *Daily Mail*, 30 July 1963.
[80] *Hansard [HC]*, 682, cols 137–9, 1 August 1963.
[81] *Sunday Telegraph*, 25 August 1963.
[82] *Daily Mirror*, 29 August 1963.
[83] PRO, ED50/862, Press Notice by the Ministry of Education, 28 August 1963.
[84] PRO, ED50/862, Boyle to Archbishop Lord Fisher, 1 October 1963.
[85] *Daily Mail*, 6 September 1963.

Parliamentary questions. When asked about the patchy provision of sex education in schools in January 1967, Denis Howell, the Joint Under-Secretary of State, simply referred the questioner to the forthcoming revision of the current health education guidelines which he hoped would 'help to produce the result which my Honourable Friend requires'.[86] The following year, after the dismissal of a medical officer at a Birmingham school, Howell was asked whether he would send a circular to all local education authorities giving guidance as to the duties appropriate to such officers 'particularly in the field of sex education'. Again he demurred, this time by stating that 'curriculum matters, including sex education, are the responsibility of local education authorities and their teachers', and he referred the questioner to the new departmental pamphlet.[87]

The pamphlets published in the 1950s and 1960s illustrate how school sex education had been constructed as a health education issue, and also reveal how the DES attempted to avoid controversy by combining both public health and moral concerns in optional guidance. The pamphlets published in 1956, 1966, and 1968 reflected the desire to placate the growing public health lobby without antagonizing moral traditionalists. After 1943, sex education guidance was always located within broader health education publications and the term 'sex education' itself did not appear on the cover of any of the pamphlets. Even inside the covers there was a tendency towards euphemism: the chapter on sex education in the 1956 pamphlet was entitled 'School and the Future Parent', and 'Moral Aspects of Health Education' in the 1966 pamphlet.[88] Emphasis was placed on the role of the family, and the recommendations on sex education were left to the discretion of individual schools.

The DES also argued that optional advice was the furthest it could reasonably go, given the legal obstacles to the development of a compulsory policy. It is true that under the 1944 Education Act, the Department did not have the statutory authority to offer anything more than guidance or suggestions on the content of curricula—sex education or otherwise. Nevertheless, this was, in reality, more of a convenient excuse than a genuine reason for inaction; legislation could have been pursued had the political will existed. The 1944 Act did impose a general duty on LEAs 'to contribute towards the spiritual, moral, mental and physical development' of school pupils,[89] but the DES did not interpret this as including a requirement for sex education. Indeed, when a Birmingham local education committee published a report on 'Sex Education in Schools' in 1967, claiming that Section 7 of the 1944 Act implied sex education was a statutory duty of local authorities,[90] the DES went out of its way to refute the claim.[91] The Chief Education Officer of the Birmingham Education Committee, Sir

[86] *Hansard [HC]*, 739, col. 638, 19 January 1967.

[87] *Hansard [HC]*, 767, cols 805–6, 27 June 1968.

[88] *Health Education*, Pamphlet No. 31, (London, 1956); *Health in Education*, Pamphlet No. 49 (London, 1966). See also *A Handbook of Health Education* (London, 1968), which was a revised version of the 1956 publication and retained the chapter heading, 'School and the Future Parent'.

[89] Education Act of 1944, Section 7.

[90] PRO, ED50/862, Birmingham Education Committee, Report of the Working Party on Sex Education, 'Sex Education in Schools', 1967.

Lionel Russell, was told by the DES 'that in the Department's view, this section, when considered in full, could not be seen as leading to the interpretation which your Authority has put on it'.[92]

The final reason for the DES's reluctance to develop a policy on school sex education was rooted in its concern to avoid conflict with the main teachers' union. The NUT supported a *laissez faire* approach, more out of a concern to protect the interests of teachers' autonomy against government intervention than a principled stance against State initiatives on sex education. The NUT was in favour of sex education but insisted that trust should be placed in the judgement of individual teachers as to whether, when, and how it should be taught. In 1944, shortly after the Board of Education had published its Pamphlet 119, the Executive of the NUT issued a statement claiming that, since there were divisions in public opinion about sex education in schools, parental consent should be obtained for such teaching as was given. The only way to ensure this was to give teachers the freedom to decide when to introduce instruction and what methods to follow.[93] Central government prescription was incompatible with this position. In 1950, the Education Committee reaffirmed the NUT's policy as set out in the 1944 statement and advised a County Association enquiry into sex education 'to take steps to ensure that any memorandum which their Education Authority might decide to issue should be in the form of advice or guidance and not in the form of a direction'.[94] The NUT's weekly newspaper, *The Schoolmaster* (renamed *The Teacher* in 1963), carried occasional articles on sex education and always recommended an advisory approach.[95] During the early 1970s, a debate over a controversial sex education film, 'Growing Up', prompted the Education Committee to report to Conference that it 'reaffirm[ed] Union policy that local education authorities should trust the professional judgement of their teachers in the selection of textbooks and visual aids'.[96] At this time, support for a *laissez faire* approach was additionally motivated by a concern that, if sex education was placed in the hands of central government, it would be shaped, even censored, according to political rather than educational needs. Thus, despite supporting the principle of sex education, the NUT did not at any stage apply pressure on the DES for a centralized or coordinated strategy. On the contrary, it insisted that teachers should be left to choose whether and what to teach themselves.

[91] PRO, ED50/862, Minute by D. R. Jones, 13 November 1967. The minute claims that such an interpretation would be in conflict with Section 23(2) of the Act.

[92] PRO, ED50/862, Jones to L. Russell, 16 November 1967; Russell to Jones, undated; Jones to Russell, 7 Febuary 1968.

[93] National Union of Teachers Archive, London (hereafter NUT), *Sex Teaching in Schools: Statement by the Executive of the National Union of Teachers*, 22 January 1944, p. 11.

[94] NUT, *81st Annual Report of the Executive of the NUT*, 1951, p. lviii.

[95] See, for example, *The Schoolmaster*: 'Sex Instruction for Juniors?', 27 January 1961; 'Sex Instruction in the Junior School', 3 March 1961; 'How to Give Juniors Sex Education', 16 June 1961; *The Teacher*: 'Brum May Teach Them Sex', 14 January 1966; 'No Uniform Methods of Teaching Sex', 20 January 1967; 'Proposal to Teach Sex in Birmingham', 20 January 1967; 'Surrey Starts Preliminary Sex Education Courses', 28 April 1967; 'Sex Education—the Teacher's Job', 28 July 1967; 'The Sex Specialists', 27 October 1967.

[96] NUT, *102nd Annual Report of the Executive of the NUT*, 1972, p. 74.

Conclusion

Policy debates are invariably shaped by the perceptions and interests of the participant actors, and, when those actors have contrasting perceptions or conflicting interests, the implications for policy-making can be profound. The politics of school sex education is a case in point. From the 1940s to 1960s, advocates for sex education in schools came largely from the ranks of doctors and public health professionals, who promoted sex education on the grounds that it was an efficacious, indeed, an essential part of the fight against VD. Convinced of its potential public health effects, and buoyed by a general enthusiasm for health education, the medical establishment viewed sex education in largely instrumental terms and by the mid-1960s was united around the need for a national policy. Given this consensus, it is hardly surprising that the Ministry of Health and its educational arm, the HEC, were in favour of sex education in schools.

In stark contrast, the Department of Education adopted a resolutely cautious approach informed by a combination of pragmatism and principle. The DES viewed sex education as a potentially explosive political issue and was far more preoccupied than the public health lobby with the moral dimensions of government intervention in this sensitive area. Important lobby groups within each department's policy orbit, including the BMA and NUT, influenced their respective positions, and it is also apparent that key individuals within the departments (figures such as Lady Birk at the HEC and Edward Boyle at the DES) themselves perceived sex education in very different ways. The non-decision-making approach of the DES was partly successful in dampening political controversy during the 1960s, but it resulted in an unresolved policy issue. The compromise arrangement—no national policy, but optional guidance on sex education located within a health education context—neither placated the public health lobby nor did it satisfy conservative critics of sex education.

The instability of this situation was partly responsible for the turbulent politics that unfolded in the 1970s only to explode in the 1980s. Following the controversies surrounding the so-called 'permissive society', especially the permissive legislation of the late 1960s, the idea that sex education offered a potential solution to the problem of VD came under attack from organizations such as The Responsible Society. These family values groups questioned the instrumental value of sex education as a public health strategy and argued that it actually contributed towards the permissive sexual attitudes and behaviour which they held responsible for the upward trends in VD, as well as a range of other social ills, including teenage pregnancy and abortion.[97] These attacks were aided by a growing uncertainty in the philosophy of public health as it was replaced by the concept of community medicine.[98] During the 1970s, the debate about sex education began to

[97] See J. Hampshire and J. Lewis, '"The Ravages of Permissiveness": Sex Education and the Permissive Society', *Twentieth Century British History*, 15 (2004), 290–312; Durham, *Sex and Politics*, pp. 5–15.

[98] J. Lewis, *What Price Community Medicine? The Philosophy, Practice and Politics of Public Health since 1991* (Brighton, 1986), pp. 100–20.

widen beyond the medical establishment and the DES, to a more public conflict between those who considered sex education as part of 'the solution' and those who saw it as part of 'the problem'. By the 1980s, this conflict was being played out in Parliament, between pressure groups such as the Sex Education Forum and the Conservative Family Campaign, and in the pages of national newspapers.[99] The refusal of the DES to adopt a more positive approach during the 1960s, as demanded by the public health lobby, may well have limited political controversy in the short term, but, by leaving a contentious policy issue unresolved, it contributed to the development of a polarized debate about school sex education that continues today.

Acknowledgements

I should like to thank the Arts and Humanities Research Board for funding the research on which this article is based (Grant: MRG-AN6026/APN12632), and express my gratitude to Jane Lewis for invaluable guidance with the project.

[99] In her studies of the 1980s and 1990s, Rachel Thomson argues that two conflicting discourses on sex education—which she labels 'public health pragmatism' and 'moral authoritarianism'—structured political debate. She also alludes to departmental conflict between Education and Health. As this article has shown, these conflicts stretch back to the post-war origins of the politics of sex education. See Thomson, 'Unholy Alliances', pp. 219–20; idem, 'Prevention, Promotion and Adolescent Sexuality', pp. 121–2.

Social History of Medicine Vol. 18 No. 1 © *The Society for the Social History of Medicine 2005, all rights reserved.*
doi:10.1093/sochis/hki005

The English Patient in Post-colonial Perspective, or Practising Surgery on the Poms

By SALLY WILDE

SUMMARY. Drawing on interviews with Australasian surgeons who trained in the 1950s and 1960s, this article discusses where, and on whom, they practised the manual skills involved in surgery. In the twentieth century, elite Australasian surgeons emphasized the importance of the science of surgery and the lengthy experience needed to acquire surgical judgement, and these concerns are reflected in the accreditation procedures adopted by the Royal Australasian College of Surgeons. However, trainee surgeons also had to acquire the manual skills that they needed in the operating theatre. The rhetoric of training emphasized the intellectual skills needed in surgery, but in reality the manual skills remained important, and there was also a fascination with the drama and stress involved in operating. In this era, British and Australasian surgical training were closely linked and many Australasian surgeons gained significant cutting experience in Britain.

KEYWORDS: surgical training, history, surgery, operating theatre, ritual, practice, Royal Australasian College of Surgeons, Royal College of Surgeons of England, patients, the gift.

Introduction

In 1965, leading English surgeon Hedley Atkins downplayed the importance of manual skills in surgery: 'The decision to operate, when to operate and what operation to do, is in nearly every circumstance more important for the patient's welfare than precisely how the operation is done.'[1] Historically, this kind of view has been associated with sayings such as 'you can teach a monkey to operate'.[2] The manual skill involved in surgery is only one component of the surgeon's craft and in Australia and New Zealand (as well as in Britain), it was commonplace to downplay either its difficulty, or its importance, or both.

'It must be recognised that the surgeon of today is not a mere craftsman', wrote Sir George Syme, one of the founders of the Royal Australasian College of Surgeons (RACS). 'He ought to be a scientist, versed in physiology and biochemistry, pathology and bacteriology, as well as anatomy. He ought to possess judgement, derived from experience, as well as technical skill.'[3] For many years, it was fashionable to describe surgery as an art and a science.[4] Clinical judgement was the

* School of History, Philosophy, Religion and Classics, University of Queensland, Queensland 4072, Australia. E-mail: *sally@wilde.net*

[1] H. Atkins, *The Surgeon's Craft* (Manchester, 1965), p. 34. Atkins was President of the Royal College of Surgeons of England 1966–9.

[2] R. W. Barnes, 'Surgical Handicraft: Teaching and Learning Surgical Skills', *American Journal of Surgery*, 153 (1987), 422–7.

[3] G. A. Syme, 'The Aims and Objects of the College of Surgeons of Australasia', *Medical Journal of Australia*, I (1928), 488–91, p. 490.

[4] For the tensions between conceptions of science and art in medicine, see C. Lawrence, 'Incommunicable Knowledge: Science, Technology and the Clinical Art in Britain 1850–1914', *Journal of*

principal 'art' of surgery and Sir Hugh Devine, another of the founders of the RACS, argued that: 'In a surgeon there is no quality of mind more to be desired than that of judgement. Judgement is the product of a mind cultured by a liberal and professional education and matured by experience. It is judgement even more than skill that makes a truly successful surgeon.'[5]

Elite Australian and New Zealand surgeons were keen to downplay the importance of operative competence alone, and to argue that they were not 'mere craftsmen', in order to distance themselves from those general practitioners who also performed surgery.[6] Theoretically, from 1932, qualification for the Fellowship of the Royal Australasian College of Surgeons (FRACS) required passing a two-part examination in the science and practice of surgery and it also required a period of surgical apprenticeship considered adequate to acquire the beginnings of the art of surgical judgement—deciding when and when not to operate, and which operation to perform.[7]

But there is a further component to learning surgery: acquiring the manual skills required to actually operate. This aspect of surgery has never been formally assessed for the FRACS, and it was not consistently taught in Australia before the 1970s.[8] Yet surgeons still somehow had to acquire the manual skills that they needed in the operating theatre. They had to become competent 'craftsmen', as well as mastering the 'art' and 'science' of surgery. In a sense, there was a gap between the rhetoric and the reality of surgical training. The rhetoric emphasized the importance of mastering the surgical sciences and acquiring clinical judgement, but, in reality, young surgeons were still focused on learning the 'knife and fork' business of operating. Although watching experienced surgeons operate and reading about surgical procedures were important, in the end surgeons learned the manual aspects of their craft (then as now) by practising.[9] Even the most basic act of cutting the skin has to be learned through practice.

Contemporary History, 20 (1985), 503–20; idem, 'Still Incommunicable: Clinical Holists and Medical Knowledge in Interwar Britain', in C. Lawrence and G. Weisz (eds), *Greater than the Parts: Holism in Biomedicine* (Oxford, 1998); J. Sadler, 'Ideologies of "Art" and "Science" in Medicine: The Transition from Medical Care to the Application of Technique in the British Medical Profession', in W. Krohn, E. T. Layton Jr, and P. Weingart (eds), *The Dynamics of Science and Technology* (Dordrecht, 1978).

[5] H. B. Devine, 'Surgical Judgement', *Australian and New Zealand Journal of Surgery*, 20 (1950), 161. On the acquisition of surgical judgement, see also C. L. Bosk, *Forgive and Remember. Managing Medical Failure* (Chicago, 1979), p. 86; K. Knafl and G. Burkett, 'Professional Socialization in a Surgical Specialty: Acquiring Medical Judgment', *Social Science and Medicine*, 9 (1975), 397–404, p. 398.

[6] S. D. Wilde, 'Practising Surgery, A History of Surgical Training in Australia 1927–74' (unpublished Ph.D. thesis, University of Melbourne, 2003).

[7] Royal Australasian College of Surgeons Archives Melbourne: Minutes and Council Papers, Se 7, (hereafter RACS Minutes and Council Papers), H. B. Devine and H. A. Newton, 'Policy in regard to the future admission of Fellows', 16 February 1932; A. W. Beasley, *The Mantle of Surgery, The First Seventy-Five Years of the Royal Australasian College of Surgeons* (Melbourne, 2002); C. Smith, 'The Shaping of the RACS 1920–60', in D. E. Theile, P. H. Carter, and C. V. Smith (eds), *Royal Australasian College of Surgeons, Handbook* (Melbourne, 1995), 13–54.

[8] In the interwar years, the Royal College of Surgeons of England did attempt to examine in operative surgery, and candidates for the Final conducted surgical procedures on cadavers. Douglas Miller described his own experience of this in 1928: D. Miller, *A Surgeon's Story* (Sydney, 1985), p. 68.

[9] For the importance of practice in the acquisition of tacit knowledge, see M. Polanyi, *Personal Knowledge* (London, 1958); idem, *The Tacit Dimension* (New York, 1967).

As one surgeon put it: 'you don't know how hard to push'.[10] Animals, cadavers, and, more recently, models, may be used for practice. But in the 1950s and 1960s, surgeons mainly learned by practising on their patients, and Australian surgeons had few opportunities even to do that.[11] Changes to training in the 1970s increased the opportunities for Australian surgeons to practise at home on Australian patients, but in the 1950s and 1960s, many went to Britain and acquired their cutting experience there, practising on National Health Service patients.

This article uses material from interviews with Australian surgeons that were conducted as a part of the research for a Ph.D. on the history of Australian surgical training.[12] During the 1950s and 1960s, a high proportion of Australian surgeons travelled to England as a part of their training. A group of surgeons who trained in this era, half of them based in Melbourne, Victoria, and half based in Brisbane, Queensland, were interviewed to supplement archival material with first-hand information on this process of 'practising on the Poms'.[13]

Surgical Accreditation

Trainee Australian surgeons did not just travel to England in search of cutting experience. They also went to take the examinations for Fellowship of the Royal College of Surgeons of England (or Edinburgh or Ireland). Australia and New Zealand followed the British pattern of accreditation by the various Royal Colleges, where bodies representing surgeons as an organized profession provided the major recognized qualifications in surgery.[14] This was different from the American pattern of accreditation, which had developed in the 1920s and 1930s. There, members of each surgical specialty (ophthalmology, orthopaedics, urology, etc.) could apply for accreditation by a dedicated specialty board, which typically included representatives from a range of bodies, not just the American College of Surgeons.[15] Although the RACS began conducting its

[10] Interview, Brisbane, 11 July 2002.

[11] E. C. Atwater, '"Making Fewer Mistakes": A History of Students and Patients', *Bulletin of the History of Medicine*, 57 (1983), 165–87, p. 187.

[12] Wilde, 'Practising Surgery'.

[13] The study was conducted under the University of Melbourne Ethics Committee Requirements, reference HREC 010412. All those doctors in a surgical training post at the Royal Melbourne Hospital in 1967 who could be traced (a total of 23) were sent a plain language statement explaining the study, and inviting them to participate. Ten agreed to do so. A group of nine surgeons who trained at the Princess Alexandra Hospital in Brisbane in the 1950s and 1960s was identified from personal contacts. They were also sent a plain language statement and all agreed to participate. Of the study participants, 15 were interviewed once and one was interviewed twice. The other three (a general surgeon, a urologist, and an ophthalmologist) formed a reference group and were interviewed on multiple occasions, separately and together.

[14] Although there were a number of specialist diplomas and degrees, most awarded by universities, their status was always problematic and the FRCS remained the benchmark qualification for a surgeon. J. Blandy and J. S. Lumley (eds), *The Royal College of Surgeons of England 200 Years of History at the Millennium* (London, 2000); J. Lister, *Postgraduate Medical Education* (London, 1993); R. Stevens, *Medical Practice in Modern England and the Impact of Specialization and State Medicine* (New Haven, 1966).

[15] L. Davis, *Fellowship of Surgeons—A History of the American College of Surgeons* (Springfield, 1966); K. M. Ludmerer, *Time to Heal, American Medical Education from the Turn of the Century to the Era of*

own examinations in the late 1940s, many Australasian surgeons continued to take the Fellowship of the Royal College of Surgeons of England (FRCS Eng) sometimes as well as, but often instead of the FRACS.[16] In its attempts to overcome this problem, the RACS imitated the Royal College of Surgeons of England.[17] Effectively, Australasian surgical training before the 1970s was still 'colonial' and heavily dependent on Britain.[18]

In the 1950s and 1960s, the FRACS and the FRCS Eng were closely-related qualifications. Both were two-part examinations, with a Primary exam in the surgical sciences of Anatomy and Physiology and a Final exam in Surgery, Surgical Anatomy, and Surgical Pathology.[19] In the 1950s and 1960s, the Primary examinations were reciprocal between the Royal Colleges of Surgeons of England, Ireland, Edinburgh, the Royal College of Physicians and Surgeons of Glasgow, and the RACS.[20] The Primary was an exceedingly tough hurdle in the basic sciences with a pass rate that was generally around 25 per cent.[21] The English College ran successful courses in the basic sciences to help candidates pass this exam, and many Commonwealth doctors travelled to London to take these courses.[22] However, candidates from a wide range of Commonwealth countries could also sit for the Royal College of Surgeons' Primary at home. In 1962, for instance, the Royal College of Surgeons of England sent examiners to Lahore, Cairo, Khartoum, Colombo, and Calcutta.[23] In addition, from 1958 the RACS conducted Primaries in Singapore, (initially under the Colombo Plan).[24] Something of the scale of the role of England in Commonwealth surgical training can be gauged from the fact that, in 1952, 20 per cent of candidates for the Final examination for the FRCS Eng (which, unlike the Primary, was always held in London) had passed the Primary elsewhere but, by 1960, this had risen to

Managed Care (New York, 1999); P. D. Olch, 'Evarts A. Graham, The American College of Surgeons, and the American Board of Surgery', *Journal of the History of Medicine*, 27 (1972), 247–61; M. M. Ravitch, *A Century of Surgery, The History of the American Surgical Association 1880–1980* (Philadelphia, 1981); J. S. Rodman, *History of the American Board of Surgery 1937–52* (Philadelphia, 1956); R. Stevens, *American Medicine and the Public Interest* (New Haven, 1971).

16 Smith, 'The Shaping of the RACS'.

17 Wilde, 'Practising Surgery'.

18 G. Basalla, 'The Spread of Western Science', *Science*, 156 (1967), 611–22.

19 RACS Archives Melbourne: Se 45 Minutes of the Fifth Annual General Meeting of the Royal Australasian College of Surgeons, 18 February 1932, p. 9.

20 RACS Minutes and Council Papers, Memorandum for the Council concerning reciprocity in Primary examinations, 24 June 1948.

21 RACS Minutes and Council Papers, S. F. Reid, 'Memorandum on the Examinations for the College', 1 June 1965. In the period 1958–63, the pass rates in the Primary averaged 25.1 per cent for the FRACS, 19.9 per cent for the FRCS England, 29.4 per cent for the FRCS Edinburgh, 26.1 per cent for the FRCS Ireland, and 25.8 per cent for the FRCS Glasgow; ibid., 17 October 1963.

22 Blandy and Lumley, *The Royal College of Surgeons of England*.

23 RACS Minutes and Council Papers, 15 March 1962.

24 The RACS held a course for the Primary in Singapore in March 1958, attended by 40 candidates: RACS Minutes and Council Papers, 21 May 1958. Initially, candidates from other Asian countries travelled to Singapore to take the Primary, but exams were later held in other centres, including Hong Kong and Kuala Lumpur. J. H. Heslop, 'The History of Basic Surgical Science Examinations in the Royal Australasian College of Surgeons', *Australian and New Zealand Journal of Surgery*, 58 (1988), 529–36.

50 per cent.[25] Besides Australia, New Zealand and South Africa, candidates came from the Indian sub-continent and South East Asia.

Unlike the Primary, the Final examinations for the FRACS and FRCS were never reciprocal, but they were still very similar. The Final of the FRCS Eng could be taken at the end of the third postgraduate year and it was always regarded as an entry qualification for the real business of surgical training: gaining supervised experience in a public hospital. This was the so-called 'apprenticeship' component of training. The Australasian fellowship, in contrast, had been envisaged by the founders of the RACS as an exit qualification; the mark of a fully qualified surgeon at the end of training.[26] Pass rates in the Final were generally higher than in the Primary, but they were still usually less than 50 per cent.

The Need to Practise

A fellowship of one of the colleges of surgeons provided accreditation, but if trainees wanted to become competent surgeons, they also needed surgical experience. As one put it: 'We had to go to England. You had two years [as a resident] and three years as a registrar, then you were out. You're not really ripe for the public at that stage.'[27] Another recalled his anxiety as a young surgeon:

> I remember quite vividly being very apprehensive when going in to operate ... almost praying that I'd be able to cope with it ... you wonder if you're good enough to cope ... that apprehension decreases with experience ... you know what you can do; you know what has to be done.[28]

As has already been noted, few senior surgeons emphasized the importance of their manual skills. On the contrary, it was common for general surgeons in particular to point out that operative competence alone did not make a good surgeon:

> The training of the young surgeon should be on two main lines. First, and most important, is that of clinical experience, clinical observation and deduction, observation of post-operative results and the correlation of the whole in one setting. The other side—that of the operation itself—although important, should be looked upon only as an incident in the whole course of the case, and should not be the climax often staged to be a striking spectacle to the uncritical.[29]

Although the Australasian Fellowship was supposed to be an 'exit' qualification at the end of training, in fact neither the Australasian nor the English Fellowship examined in operative competence.[30] As one surgeon put it: 'I got my Fellowship

[25] RACS Minutes and Council Papers, Report on reciprocity in exams with RCS Eng, 15 March 1962.

[26] H. B. Devine, 'Fellowship of the Royal Australasian College of Surgeons', *Australian and New Zealand Journal of Surgery*, 18 (1948), 57–60.

[27] Interview, Brisbane, 11 July 2002.

[28] Interview, Brisbane, 11 July 2002.

[29] R. B. Wade, 'Surgical Training', *Australian and New Zealand Journal of Surgery*, 3 (1934), 289–91, p. 289.

[30] In contrast to the Fellowship of the American College of Surgeons, which was initially based on reports of surgical competence, rather than examination. See L. Davis, *Fellowship of Surgeons*.

and no-one, apart from my own peers here . . . knew whether I could operate.'[31] It follows that substantial operative experience was not strictly necessary in order to pass either the English or the Australasian Fellowship, although it almost certainly did make it somewhat easier to pass the Final. 'They could ask questions about operative technique during the exam and an experienced person could tell whether you knew what you were talking about.'[32] Generally, however, trainees did not want operative experience in order to help them pass the examinations. They wanted operative experience while they were still under some sort of supervision, so that when they went into practice on their own they were competent to deal with the problems that came their way. What they wanted to avoid was precisely the position reported by one Melbourne surgeon who said: 'suddenly you're a consultant and you're doing operations you've never done before'.[33]

Generally speaking, surgeons like to operate. Douglas Miller argued that he became interested in surgery while an undergraduate: 'It was all very exciting, and I found myself fascinated by surgical technique and enjoying the drama of it all.'[34] One surgeon said that he enjoyed surgery: 'I enjoyed the doing.'[35] Another argued that surgeons are happy when they are performing surgery and feel that they are doing good.[36] In the North American context, Joan Cassell quoted one surgeon who reported that his pulse rose from 70 to 135 while he was operating.[37] In 1975, American surgeon Owen Wangensteen wrote that: 'There is probably a time in every young surgeon's life when he would rather operate than eat or sleep.'[38]

The acquisition of manual skills may not have received much emphasis from senior surgeons, but at some stage it loomed large in the consciousness of virtually all trainees. Exactly why is tied up with the peculiar nature of an occupation that involves one human being legally cutting another. In 1991, Stefan Hirschauer noted that observational studies of operating theatres were surprisingly rare.[39] He went on to cite studies by Erving Goffman, Pearl Katz, Joan Cassell, and R. Wilson.[40] There have also been important studies by Charles Bosk and Nick Fox.[41] But if observational studies of operating theatres are still relatively

[31] Interview, Brisbane, 11 July 2002.

[32] Interview, Brisbane, 11 July 2002.

[33] Interview, Melbourne, 25 October 2001.

[34] D. Miller, *A Surgeon's Story*, p. 18.

[35] Interview, Melbourne, 26 October 2001.

[36] Interview, Brisbane, 17 July 2002.

[37] J. Cassell, 'On Control, Certitude, and the "Paranoia" of Surgeons', *Culture, Medicine and Psychiatry*, 11 (1987), 229–49, pp. 232, 234.

[38] O. H. Wangensteen and S. D. Wangensteen, 'The Surgical Amphitheatre, History of its Origins, Functions and Fate', *Surgery*, 77 (1975), 403–18, p. 415.

[39] S. Hirschauer, 'The Manufacture of Bodies in Surgery', *Social Studies of Science*, 21 (1991), 279–319, p. 280.

[40] Cassell, 'On Control, Certitude, and the "Paranoia" of Surgeons'; E. Goffman, *Encounters, Two Studies in the Sociology of Interaction* (Harmondsworth, 1961); P. Katz, 'Ritual in the Operating Room', *Ethnology*, 20 (1981), 335–50; R. Wilson, 'Teamwork in the Operating Room', *Human Organization*, 12 (1954), 9–14.

[41] Bosk, *Forgive and Remember*; N. J. Fox, *The Social Meaning of Surgery* (Milton Keynes, 1992); idem, 'Space, Sterility and Surgery: Circuits of Hygiene in the Operating Theatre', *Social Science*

rare, they far outnumber studies of other aspects of surgical work, such as ward rounds and out-patient consultations.[42] In contrast to surgeons themselves, who emphasize the importance of other aspects of their work, operative surgery seems to have held a particular fascination for scholars interested in the work and culture of surgeons. Recurring themes include the intersections between drama, ritual, power, taboo, and the procedures associated with aseptic surgery.[43]

In 1994, Harry Collins criticized the emphasis on ritual in a number of these studies and made the simple point that strangers entering an operating theatre might read what they see as ritual, but to those who work in operating theatres, much of what takes place there is simply routine.[44] It was an operating theatre nurse who pointed out that operating theatre life is even more routine for nurses (and presumably orderlies and anaesthetists) than it is for surgeons.[45] That is where they spend their working days, day in, day out, while surgeons (and trainee surgeons) come and go from office consultations, out-patients' clinics, and ward rounds.

Partly, the discussion of ritual versus routine hinges on definitions. While surgery might be a transforming event for the patient, analogous to the rites of passage discussed by anthropologists such as Victor Turner, the patient is not transformed by the ritual/routine of the operating theatre.[46] The patient is transformed by the matter-of-fact business of cutting and sewing. Surgery is not what Bourdieu has called a rite of consecration or institution, with symbolic efficacy, but is, of itself, for the patient, potentially a transforming experience.[47] Writers such as David Kertzer and David Cannadine have taken a rather different view of ritual and shown how it can be used to obtain and retain power and status.[48] This is not inconsistent with the view of what happens in surgery adopted by both Nick Fox and Harry Collins. They disagree with each other,

and Medicine, 45 (1997), 649–57. See also J. Cassell, The Woman in the Surgeon's Body (Cambridge, MA, 1998); P. Katz, *The Scalpel's Edge, The Culture of Surgeons* (Boston, 1999); L. Jordanova, *Sexual Visions: Images of Gender in Science and Medicine between the Eighteenth and Twentieth Centuries* (Madison, 1989), especially ch. 7; M. E. Felker, 'Ideology and Order in the Operating Room', in L. Romanucci-Ross, D. E. Moerman, and L. R. Tancredi (eds), *The Anthropology of Medicine, From Culture to Method* (Cambridge, MA, 1983), 349–65.

[42] For studies of surgical ward rounds, see C. L. Bosk, 'Occupational Rituals in Patient Management', *New England Journal of Medicine*, 303 (1980), 71–6; N. J. Fox, 'Discourse, Organisation and the Surgical Ward Round', *Sociology of Health and Illness*, 15 (1993), 16–42. For a study of the medical examination, see K. Young, 'Disembodiment: The Phenomenology of the Body in Medical Examinations', *Semiotica*, 73 (1989), 43–66; idem, *Presence in the Flesh—The Body in Medicine* (Cambridge, MA, 1997).

[43] See the debate between Collins and Hirschauer, H. M. Collins, 'Dissecting Surgery: Forms of Life Depersonalized', *Social Studies of Science*, 24 (1994), 311–33; Hirschauer, 'The Manufacture of Bodies in Surgery'. For a surgeon's view of operating theatres and rituals, see Wangensteen and Wangensteen, 'The Surgical Amphitheatre'.

[44] Collins, 'Dissecting Surgery', p. 311.

[45] J. Rabach, personal communication.

[46] V. W. Turner, *The Ritual Process* (London, 1969).

[47] P. Bourdieu, *Language and Symbolic Power*, J. B. Thompson (ed.), G. Raymond and M. Adamson (trans.) (Cambridge, 1991), pp. 117–19.

[48] D. Cannadine, 'Splendor out of Court: Royal Spectacle and Pageantry in Modern Britain, *c.* 1820–1977', in S. Wilentz (ed.), *Rites of Power: Symbolism, Ritual and Politics Since the Middle Ages* (Philadelphia, 1985); D. I. Kertzer, *Ritual, Politics and Power* (New Haven, 1988).

but they do agree that at least some of what goes on in operating theatres is about reinforcing the power, status, and authority of surgeons.[49] There is some evidence that this was the case in Australia in the 1950s and 1960s:

> I've seen Mr (...) pick up a tray of instruments and say: 'sister if you don't mend your ways I'm going to throw these instruments against the wall' and she said: 'but you can't do that Mr (...)' and he said: 'right, you watch me', and over they went.[50]

Similar behaviour is reported of other surgeons. For instance, a nurse who trained in Melbourne in the 1960s reported being at the centre of a power battle between the surgeon and the theatre sister, during which the surgeon threw every instrument she handed him onto the floor.[51] But operating theatres can also be sites for heightened tension, and a number of the stories that surgeons tell about their training concern the management of stress, rather than the exercise of power:

> In an operating theatre you'll see the best and the worst of human emotions. ... I tried at all times to show respect to those who were working with me. ... Sometimes things don't go right ... the pathology at hand had made things difficult ... you would see all the emotions, good and bad. ... I never threw anything—I might swear. I tried to act as though my mother was there—she always behaved impeccably ... if I heard a registrar joking in the operating theatre, I'd tell him to watch his step or he's out the door. ... Some men can be very rude to the operating theatre staff.[52]

Most of surgery is routine, '70–80 per cent of everybody's work is absolutely routine',[53] but a number of surgeons argued that you could identify moments of tension by silence: 'you'll hear conversation cease, this is the crunch bit'.[54] 'Some can talk in theatre, some can't; it's a personality thing ... an anaesthetist who had seen me ever since my resident days knew when to talk, when to shut up; we'd talk about opera and so on.'[55] In his autobiography, Sir Benjamin Rank, a plastic surgeon at the Royal Melbourne Hospital in this era, agreed on the importance of the anaesthetist:

> Len [Travers] was not only good at his job, he was also good for me. In early years, I was edgy in the operating room and consequently a trying person to work with. Those around me often took the brunt for conditions not of their making. At such times Len knew the value of silence, of a quiet gulp or of simply telling me to shut up and get on with it.[56]

Within this environment, where the atmosphere varied from the mundane to high drama depending on the nature of the procedure and the personality of the senior surgeon, trainees learned by watching. Australian trainees may have generally spent much more time assisting—holding a retractor and observing surgery—than they spent being assisted to perform the surgery themselves. But this does

[49] Collins, 'Dissecting Surgery', p. 319; N. J. Fox, 'Fabricating Surgery: A Response to Collins', *Social Studies of Science*, 24 (1994), 347–54, p. 349.
[50] Interview, Melbourne, 12 November 2001.
[51] Interview, Brisbane, 6 July 2002.
[52] Interview, Brisbane, 17 July 2002.
[53] Interview, Brisbane, 30 July 2002.
[54] Interview, Brisbane, 11 July 2002.
[55] Interview, Melbourne, 12 November 2001.
[56] B. K. Rank, *Heads and Hands, an Era of Plastic Surgery* (London, 1987).

not mean that they did not learn a very great deal. Watching was considered to be vitally important preparation for when trainees came to perform the procedure themselves:

Evan Thomson taught me to write my own text-book of surgery—he counted every movement—he was absolutely brilliant, bloodless, gentle in handling tissues ... I used to write down what movements you needed to do a gall bladder, what movements you needed to do a hernia.[57]

For America, Charles Bosk has emphasized the importance of the variations in the way a particular surgical procedure is performed for the process of training. Fully-qualified surgeons can make up their own minds about how to perform a procedure, but in training they have to do it the way their chief wants.[58] This also applied to Australia.

In terms of operating, I'm going to do everything first up and show them how I do it ... I say 'I know you've done a bit of operating around the place, but I'm going to show you what I want ...' so I do the operation ... 'so this is how you do a hand sutured single layer anastomosis—you put the first stitch in at the back and the reason you do that in that position is that because if you don't the muscle slips away', and so on—so all the tricks that I have learned I show him ... 'this is what I want you to do when you're with me. Down the track a bit you'll take the best of what you see' [and make up your own mind what to do].[59]

However, trainee surgeons wanted to operate themselves, not just watch and assist, and they wanted to take on the more difficult and interesting cases, not just the routine appendecectomies and hernia repairs that their chiefs allowed them to perform in Australia. The consequence of this was an inherent potential for tension between trainees and consultants. Trainees wanted to practise (under supervision) and consultants found it easier and less stressful to do the surgery themselves. The problem for the trainees was that the consultants controlled access to surgical experience and, especially, to supervised elective surgical experience.

'You Can't do this Operation Until You've Done Ten of Them'[60]

The lack of hands-on operating experience is a frequent theme of the stories that Australian surgeons tell about their training in the 1950s and 1960s. As one recalled: 'When I was progressing through the Australian system, the main deficiency was practical hands-on training.'[61] Another said that in Melbourne's teaching hospitals it was 'unlikely even an appendix would be done by an incompletely qualified individual',[62] while a Brisbane surgeon said that 'there isn't any doubt that in the 1950s and 1960s the overwhelming majority of cases were done by the consultants'.[63]

[57] Interview, Brisbane, 23 July 2002.
[58] Bosk, *Forgive and Remember.* See especially 'Quasi-normative errors', pp. 61–7.
[59] Interview, Brisbane, 30 July 2002.
[60] Saying current at the Royal Melbourne Hospital in the 1960s.
[61] Interview, Melbourne, 25 October 2001.
[62] Interview, Melbourne, 8 November 2001.
[63] Interview, Brisbane, 11 July 2002.

There are three main roles that trainee surgeons may take in the operating theatre: assisting and watching a senior surgeon; operating themselves with the assistance of an experienced surgeon; and performing surgery alone. By the 1970s it was believed that, ideally, trainees performed these roles in succession with each new surgical procedure that they learned.[64] However, in the 1950s and 1960s, trainee Australian surgeons were given few opportunities to play the second role: operating themselves with the assistance of an experienced surgeon.

In this era there was much talk of surgical apprenticeships, although what exactly that meant seems to have varied considerably by State and by hospital. However, in so far as the phrase implies a direct one-to-one relationship between a master and an apprentice, with the former taking responsibility for training the latter, surgical apprenticeship is a profoundly misleading way of describing the process of acquiring surgical experience in Australia in the 1950s and 1960s. With a few exceptions, aspiring surgeons were, as one put it, very much more like surgical journeymen, picking up their tools and travelling from one master to another, gaining experience (and if they were lucky, training) wherever they could.[65] In Melbourne and Adelaide, the old-style, unpaid type of apprentices typically had an honorary appointment at a public hospital and assisted their chief in his private practice.[66] They were generally allowed to perform a wider range of surgery in the public hospital than the paid registrar type of 'apprentices', but neither model of surgical training incorporated a commitment of much time by the senior surgeon to assisting when the trainee was performing surgery.

In the recent history of the Royal College of Surgeons of England, it was argued that during the Second World War: 'A new concept crept in ... that surgical skills could be taught practically, not merely by holding a retractor.'[67] The idea of hands-on skills training for surgeons supposedly followed the training developed for RAF Spitfire pilots. This may be the case, but it does not seem to have followed that many senior surgeons thought that they ought to be involved in providing this kind of training, at least in Australia and New Zealand. Of the immediate post-war period, New Zealand surgeon Rowan Nicks wrote: 'In those days of apprentice training little encouragement was given to personal supervised training of assistants.'[68] Senior surgeons seem to have preferred what might be characterized as the surgical version of 'chalk and talk', encouraging trainees to watch and assist them. This was considered an appropriate method for passing on intellectual skills. However, the trainees also needed to acquire the requisite manual skills and most of them performed some

[64] Interviews, Brisbane, 11 and 30 July 2002.

[65] Interview, Brisbane, 4 April 2002.

[66] Interview, Melbourne, 26 November 2001.

[67] Blandy and Lumley, *The Royal College of Surgeons of England*, p. 45.

[68] R. Nicks, *The Dance of Life. The Life and Times of an Antipodean Surgeon* (Melbourne, 1996), p. 55.

emergency surgery alone, especially at night. 'You were taught by a registrar older than yourself with emergency surgery.'[69]

> There was an enormous amount of cutting here to do ... but only a limited amount was given to the juniors ... enormous lists, no overtime, you worked until the work was finished—tough on the nurses. As you got better you were allocated lesser surgery, usually unsupervised—hernias, piles, varicose veins, removal of simple lumps, might even do a gall bladder ... amputations in orthopaedics ... there was a time constraint. Registrars are slower.[70]

But senior surgeons did not often take any steps to train young doctors by assisting them to perform elective surgery.[71] As one Brisbane surgeon put it: 'They'd let you do operations, but they wouldn't assist you.'[72] The reasons for this varied from surgeon to surgeon and from trainee to trainee. At the Royal Melbourne Hospital, registrars usually rotated through a range of surgical specialties, spending three or four months in each. One surgeon outlined some of the reasons why none of the senior surgeons in these units allowed him any hands-on experience:

> [In thoracic surgery] it was conventional for registrars if they really took the boss's eye to do one thoracotomy—to open the chest on one occasion. I never quite got to do that. I did very little [in plastic surgery. The boss] didn't have a high opinion of my skills. The thoracic surgeon ... did, but he just felt scared about anybody but himself operating, and the neurosurgeon—well, I wasn't up to any neurosurgery much—it was purely assisting.[73]

Surgeons were concerned with results and felt under no obligation to assist and supervise a trainee who wanted to perform a major operation. For many years, it has been acknowledged that the task of supervising trainee surgeons requires enormous patience and self-restraint. One recent American textbook on surgical ethics suggested that supervising surgeons should be paid extra for the task. The supervisor is 'there both to teach the resident and to protect the patient. This supervising role often takes a great deal more skill, emotional toll, and effort than would be expended by simply performing the procedure oneself'.[74] Few senior Australian surgeons of the 1950s and 1960s, it seems, had the patience to let trainees perform many operations themselves. Trainees, generally speaking, operate very much more slowly than experienced surgeons. As a Melbourne surgeon put it: 'Mr (...) would take an abdominal resection fast. He wasn't going to wait around while I did it.'[75]

[69] Interview, Brisbane, 17 July 2002.
[70] Interview, Brisbane, 11 July 2002.
[71] Interviews, Melbourne, 25 October, 8 and 12 November 2001; interviews, Brisbane, 4 April, 11 and 17 July 2002.
[72] Interview, Brisbane, 23 July 2002.
[73] Interview, Melbourne, 12 November 2001.
[74] L. B. McCullough, J. W. Jones, and B. A. Brody (eds), *Surgical Ethics* (New York, 1998), p. 330.
[75] Interview, Melbourne, 12 November 2001.

Practising on the Poms

The pattern of travelling to Britain to sit for the FRCS has already been described, but the other major attraction of Britain was that it offered a large number of short-term positions for registrars within the National Health Service. The number of posts for consultant surgeons in Britain was tightly limited. Young British surgeons could remain as senior registrars for years waiting for a vacancy. Consequently, the number of young British doctors opting for a surgical career did not match the relatively large number of junior surgeons in training needed to staff the NHS. Broadly speaking, overseas doctors, including Australians, filled these short-term posts.[76] There were few career prospects for them in Britain, but this did not matter to those who were using these junior positions to provide themselves with experience, before returning to their country of origin.[77]

A typical pattern was to obtain a position as a ship's surgeon and travel to England by sea.[78] If the Primary had not been passed in Australia, the first task was to attend the course run by the Royal College of Surgeons of England in Lincoln's Inn Fields, while living next door at Nuffield College. Passing the examinations in England was considered by some to be easier than in Australia, but it was still difficult, and there are many, many stories of repeated attempts, finally crowned by success. The porter at the Royal College of Surgeons in London used to tell candidates that they only needed two things to pass the exams: a hammer and a nail, so that they could nail their scrotum to a chair and study.[79]

Some Australians went on to study for the Final straight after passing the Primary, but others took a position in a British hospital and locum jobs seem to have been fairly easy to get.[80] Aspiring surgeons then rolled up their sleeves for a stint of what was sometimes referred to as 'practising on the Poms'.

> You'd practise on the Poms . . . the equivalent of the whole population of Australia lived in London. Every hospital had lots of patients; the consultants were not keen to come in at night. . . . We were receiving every other night . . . got bone injuries as well as hernias and appendices.[81]

> England was where you got the cutting . . . you needed a good two years in England. There was a different philosophy, that in the NHS [the patients] took [their] chances. The attitude was 'they're all trained surgeons; you can't have an experienced surgeon for everything.'[82]

> In Brisbane the residents didn't do anything of any consequence. If you wanted to get cutting you had to get to England. I had my own list in North Wales, but you had to

[76] Atkins, *The Surgeon's Craft*, pp. 37–59.

[77] Heslop, 'The History of Basic Surgical Science Examinations in the Royal Australasian College of Surgeons'.

[78] Interviews, Melbourne, 22 and 26 October 2001; Brisbane, 23 July 2002.

[79] Interview, Brisbane, 23 July 2002.

[80] Interviews, Melbourne, 22 October, 26 October and 9 November 2001; Brisbane, 11 and 17 July 2002.

[81] Interview, Melbourne, 22 October 2001.

[82] Interview, Melbourne, 12 November 2001.

be known, you had to have been observed, you had to have the Primary. ... No matter where you went out of London you could get experience.[83]

If you had your English Fellowship you wouldn't be regarded as a consultant surgeon, but you could do a reasonable number of operations reasonably well and the English population were very amenable and if you'd say: 'you need your stomach taking out', they'd say 'when, doctor?' They wouldn't ask you why it was necessary or 'aren't you too young to be doing this sort of thing?' They just accepted that if you're on the staff of a teaching hospital as a surgeon you knew what you were doing. In actual fact you didn't half the time, but that's what they thought.[84]

I wanted to get cutting experience so I volunteered to do an extra operating session on Saturday. They had a ten-year waiting list for hernias. I wanted to learn varicose veins. So I used to operate like mad, really, in England. [Once the consultants saw that he was competent, they allowed him to do most of the surgery.] I ran Rugby Hospital for two years to my heart's content and I had a ball, basically.[85]

Conclusion

Trainee surgeons needed to practise and, in the 1950s and 1960s, many Australasian surgeons practised on English patients. Surgical training, of course, was just a particular instance of the broader medical training paradigm that was based on the availability of patients who were prepared to allow themselves to be used for teaching purposes.[86] In 1970, Richard Titmuss published his well-known (and controversial) book on blood as gift and blood as commodity.[87] Towards the end, he raised the issue of other instances of gifts to strangers and non-economic transactions, and floated ideas of other books he might have written:

We could, for example, have taken for study the giving role of the patient as 'teaching material', and as research material for experimentation and the testing of new drugs and other diagnostic and therapeutic measures. Millions of people in Western societies every year are expected to give themselves, without price or a contractual reward, in these situations. ... To qualify as a doctor in Britain, it is probable that the average medical student now needs access to or contact with in one form or another some 300 different patients. ... They are no longer 'charity' patients and could not in the 1970s, whatever the future of the National Health Service, be treated as such. Should their contribution to medical education, therefore, be paid on market criteria?[88]

[83] Interview, Brisbane, 4 April 2002.

[84] Interview, Brisbane, 11 July 2002.

[85] Interview, Brisbane, 23 July 2002.

[86] S. C. Lawrence, *Charitable Knowledge: Hospital Pupils and Practitioners in Eighteenth-century London* (Cambridge, 1996); E. Ackerknecht, *Medicine at the Paris Hospital, 1794–1848* (Baltimore, 1967); M. Foucault, *The Birth of the Clinic*, A. Sheridan (trans.) (New York, 1973); V. Nutton and R. Porter (eds), *The History of Medical Education in Britain* (Amsterdam, 1995); T. N. Bonner, *Becoming a Physician, Medical Education in Britain, France, Germany, and the United States, 1750–1945* (New York, 1995).

[87] For some of the debates over Titmuss' work, see J. G. Allen, 'Comments on Titmuss-Anderson-Surgenor Debate over The Gift Relationship', *International Journal of Health Services*, 3 (1973), 519–20. For seminal ideas on the gift relationship, see M. Mauss, *The Gift. The Form and Reason for Exchange in Archaic Societies*, W. D. Halls (trans.) (New York, 1990).

[88] R. Titmuss, *The Gift Relationship* (London, 1970), pp. 213–14.

It would appear that Titmuss saw a difference between 'charity' patients whose contribution to medical education was, by implication, appropriate (in return for their care), and National Health Service patients. In her study of the 'New York Hospital', Sandra Opdycke noted: 'In earlier years, a stay on a New York Hospital ward had represented a clear trade: the patient provided the hospital with clinical material and, in exchange, received free care.'[89] The exact nuances of which patients were considered appropriate for training varied by country and by time, but broadly in Britain and Australasia in the twentieth century, public patients were considered appropriate for training, and private patients were not. Although exceptions to this pattern are not hard to find, the basic paradigm was a tacit understanding that public patients owed something to the doctors or the nurses or the hospital in return for their treatment. This gift relationship was most obvious where no money changed hands—when, for instance, honorary surgeons and physicians at charitable hospitals treated (poor) patients for free.[90] But, by the 1950s, this was no longer the position in either Britain or Australasia. As Titmuss pointed out, NHS hospitals were not charitable hospitals. They were paid for from taxes, not private philanthropy, and the doctors were paid to work there. In Australia in the 1950s and 1960s, the position was more complicated. While all of Australia's major public hospitals received considerable government funding (as well as philanthropic donations), in some states, including Queensland, doctors were paid for their work in public hospitals, while in others, including Victoria, their appointments were honorary and unpaid. In most States, including Victoria, many public hospital patients also made a direct financial contribution to the cost of their care.[91] But in both Britain and Australia, teaching hospitals were almost exclusively public hospitals (in contrast to the position in North America where major private clinics were also teaching institutions).[92]

This article has focused on trainee Australasian surgeons and some of the reasons for their limited access to 'cutting' experience in Australia and New Zealand. In an interesting post-colonial twist on what might, perhaps, be the expected relationship, in the 1950s and 1960s Australian and New Zealand surgeons (and indeed, young doctors from all over the Commonwealth) practised their surgery on British National Health Service patients. However, this article has not addressed the issue of why it was easier to gain access to practical surgical experience in Britain. Was this because of differences between Australasia and Britain in attitudes towards the mentoring role of the surgical teacher? Or could it possibly reflect differing attitudes in their respective health systems

[89] S. Opdycke, *No One Was Turned Away, The Role of Public Hospitals in New York City since 1900* (New York, 1999), p. 108.

[90] R. Porter, 'The Gift Relation: Philanthropy and Provincial Hospitals in Eighteenth-century England', in L. Granshaw and R. Porter (eds), *The Hospital in History* (London, 1989); L. Granshaw, 'Introduction', in J. Barry and C. Jones (eds), *Medicine and Charity Before the Welfare State* (London, 1991); A. J. Kidd, 'Philanthropy and the "Social History Paradigm"', *Social History*, 21 (1996), 180–92.

[91] Wilde, 'Practising Surgery'.

[92] Ludmerer, *Time to Heal*; Stevens, *American Medicine*.

towards practising surgery on public hospital patients? Surgical trainees could not become competent surgeons without patients to practise on, and variations by time and place in what has been considered to be the appropriate role of the patient in surgical training perhaps deserve further examination.

Acknowledgements

I would like to thank all the surgeons in Brisbane and Melbourne who took part in this project and who so generously gave their time and expertise to read and comment on what I have written about their training. None of them should be held responsible for the views expressed by the author or for any errors in the text.

Social History of Medicine Vol. 18 No. 1 © The Society for the Social History of Medicine 2005, all rights reserved.
doi:10.1093/sochis/hki008–hki023

Book Reviews

E. Magnello and A. Hardy (eds), *The Road to Medical Statistics*, Amsterdam: Rodopi, 2002. Pp. xi + 155. £25.00 (pbk). ISBN 9 0420 1597 7.

While this book focuses on the development of the idea and practice of medical statistics, it also has many lessons for other areas of historical endeavour and therefore deserves to be on reading-lists and bookshelves. Magnello and Hardy begin the volume with a discussion of the difference between statistics, medical statistics, vital statistics, and quantification, noting that mathematical statistics did not gain primacy until the twentieth century. The volume then moves on to an essay by Phillip Kraeger which focuses on the place of rhetoric in vital measurement by examining Graunt's methods. Kraeger argues that this illustrates rhetoric, both being used as a tool that made mathematical and quantitative advances such as classification and probability 'understandable and compelling' and as part of an early modern discipline which combined mathematics, book-keeping, classification, and rhetorical comparison. Andrea Rusnock takes up some of these themes, with an intriguing examination of Thomas Nettleton's early eighteenth-century attempts to increase the take-up of smallpox inoculation using his 'merchant logick'. The same accounting process was used to solve the dilemma of whether to treat the poor in hospitals or their own homes in the late eighteenth century, once the battle for a positive view of inoculation had been won. Other essays focus on national accounts, dealing with the changing content and format of the Annual Reports of the Registrar General between 1837 and 1920, with Edward Higgs suggesting that simple political decisions, and, crucially, the administrative and personal competence of key staff, explain the changing format of the Reports.

John Senior returns to micro-level statistical methods, by investigating the role of quantification and statistics in the rise of neurology, and in particular electro-therapy. He traces the debate between those who wished to quantify the relationship between dosage and outcome using the galvanometer and those who saw the patient as an individual and the practitioner as the best judge of the relationship between dosage and outcome. Eileen Magnello examines the relationship between mathematical statistics and medical research in the competing work of Karl Pearson and his followers, and Austin Bradford Hill, with a particular emphasis on the differences between vital statistics and mathematical statistics, as embodied in the work of Pearson and Hill. Rosser Matthews builds on these foundations by looking at the conflict between medicine as art and medicine as science, and how this was mediated by twentieth-century biometricians, with a particular focus on debates over the value of vaccine therapy for typhoid and pneumonia, between Almroth Wright and the followers of Karl Pearson.

All these chapters have merit in their own right, and the book also makes a contribution to a sphere of medical history which is greater than the sum of its parts. This may be enough for some readers, but the real merit for social historians of medicine might be that many of the lessons that spring from its pages are portable to many other debates. Three lessons spring easily to mind. First, several of the papers concentrate on the shaping of debate and practice from the standpoint of investigations of the life and work of particular individuals. This is more than simple biography and it works. In this sense, it is unfortunate that the radical individual as a mover and shaker has disappeared below the horizon of many debates in the social history of medicine. Secondly, while Rusnock's chapter may have been supplanted by her book, the idea of merchant logic has relevance for other areas. Finally, this book is not about the practice of quantification *per se*, but rather about the process by which statistics became acceptable and then colonized the practice and conception of medicine.

STEVEN KING

Oxford Brookes University
doi: 10.1093/sochis/hki008

David E. Allen and Gabriele Hatfield, *Medicinal Plants in Folk Tradition: An Ethnobotany of Britain and Ireland*, Cambridge: Timber Press, 2004. Pp. 396. £22.50 (pbk). ISBN 0 8819 2638.

This is an eagerly awaited medical compendium that summarizes all recorded folk medical uses for wild plants in Britain, Ireland, and the Isle of Man. Both authors are well-respected botanists and historians and their combined effort has produced an important reference tool which will be of interest to historians of medicine, as well as ethnobotanists. The purported purpose of the book is 'to demonstrate that a large enough body of evidence has survived to show that the folk medical tradition was impressively wide in its botanical reach and equally impressive in the range of ailments treated' (p. 25).

This is a well-researched book. The authors have referred to some 300 published and unpublished texts in addition to data collected both by individuals and by organizations such as the Irish Folklore Commission. The end result is that over 400 plants are grouped by family in chapters from mosses and lichens to trees and flowering plants accompanied by summaries of distribution, country of origin, and the medical complaints that each could treat. Regretfully, entries do not always identify all counties and locations reported, especially where there is frequent use of a particular plant, which makes it somewhat difficult to assess the relative importance of such plants. However, the great strength of this book is that every specific use reported is referenced for further research. The volume also includes a full bibliography and indexes. While the authors show an awareness of difficult issues, such as the problem of naming and the accurate identification of plants, they have tended to use terms from the original. The latter has been effectively updated.

Overall, this is an attractively produced and readable book which is likely to have wide appeal, especially for academics interested in the collection of data on oral traditions such as the National Institute for Medical Herbalists' 'Ethnomedica Project'. However, while this book provides much valuable information, there is a great deal more work that remains to be done on the connections between folk and learned medical traditions.

ANNE STOBART

Middlesex University
doi: 10.1093/sochis/hki009

Ken Arnold and D. Olsen (eds), *Medicine Man: The Forgotten Museum of Henry Wellcome*, London: British Museum Press, 2003. Pp. 397. £19.99 (pbk). ISBN 0 7141 2794 9.

This book is a compilation of beautiful and provoking images of objects, accompanied by a series of articles from the Wellcome Historical Medical Museum. The superb selection and quality of the images provide a tantalizing view of the scope and quality of the items collected by Henry Wellcome, many of which are displayed in London at the Science Museum and the British Library. These include various works of art and objects spanning the centuries, and are representative of different societies and cultures. Arnold and Olsen have chosen a number of interesting and informative essays focusing on other aspects of the Wellcome collection. These include an introductory essay by

Ghislaine Lawrence, followed by an examination by Frances Knights as to how the collection came into being. The book also contains pieces on the archaeological collections by Chris Gosden, another on the anthropological collection by John Mack, and two essays by John Pickstone and Ruth Richardson. The major importance of Arnold and Olsen's book rests on the array of fascinating illustrations it contains. As such, it will probably be of greatest interest to those interested in medical anthropology or art. However, the volume will also be a useful work for students of museology, as well as for those working in museums. Although the essays help to convince readers of the importance of the collection, a more in-depth examination of its renaissance and later fate would have been welcome.

KEVIN FLUDE

Old Operating Theatre, Museum and Herb Garret, London
doi: 10.1093/sochis/hki010

Hera Cook, *The Long Sexual Revolution; English Women, Sex and Contraception 1800–1975*, Oxford: Oxford University Press, 2004. Pp. xiv + 412. £35.00 (pbk). ISBN 0 1992 5239 4.

This book offers an account of changing patterns of sexual behaviour and contraceptive use among the English between 1800 and 1975, and provides a valuable and refreshing contribution to the literature on the history of family planning. It is written from a female perspective, and explores major issues that have affected the sexual autonomy of women. Cook addresses a wide spectrum of sexual behaviours and contraceptive practices, and examines an evolving subculture based on wide-ranging and thorough research. The text includes interesting supporting quotations with insights into women's lore, and is a valuable resource for both medical historians and health care professionals.

'Inventing contraception', the first of three sections, addresses some of the underlying causes of fluctuations in national fertility rates after the peak in early nineteenth-century gross reproduction rates. Cook discusses why fertility rates declined before acceptable methods of contraception could have had a significant effect, revealing a wide range of underlying influences which reduced sexual activity among females from social, economic, cultural, and biological perspectives. The double standard in sexual behaviour for males and females are clearly evident. The author also draws attention to class distinctions in contraceptive use and general female ignorance of sexual matters. Specific contemporary methods of contraception are discussed, including the widely practised withdrawal method and sexual abstinence.

The second section discusses advice on sexual matters found in contemporary 'sex manuals', and examines the changing nature of female sexual repression as illustrated by increasingly explicit sex manuals that attempted to reconcile women with the genitalia, from which they became culturally alienated, and encouraged them to acknowledge their sexual needs as well as their own physical and emotional capabilities for enjoying intercourse. There is also an appendix containing a brief analysis of large numbers of sex manuals and the backgrounds of their authors.

The final part of the book is called 'The English Sexual Revolution' and discusses the effects upon the lives of women of the introduction of the oral contraceptive pill. Using supporting demographic data, which shows that as pill use escalated, so did birth rates, Cook revisits one of her original questions posed in the introduction about whether the pill liberated women. She argues that the pill promoted greater sexual equality between males and females and permitted women more freedom to express their sexual desires and engage in a wider range of erotic experiment without invariably risking pregnancy. Males, meanwhile, continued to assume the dominant role in heterosexual relationships and coerced women into agreeing to sexual intercourse, simply because the latter were on the pill.

JANETTE ALLOTEY

University of Manchester
doi: 10.1093/sochis/hki011

Joel Peter Eigen, *Unconscious Crime: Mental Absence and Criminal Responsibility in Victorian London*, Baltimore, MD: The Johns Hopkins University Press, 2003. Pp. xii + 223. $39.95 (hbk). ISBN 0 8018 7428 9.

This book makes an important contribution to our understanding of the complex relationship between the legal system and the medical profession between 1843 and 1876, when defence through insanity was significantly but controversially expanded. It complements Eigen's earlier work which examined the origins of such testimony. Eigen has revisited the Old Bailey Session Papers and has again shown the value of this resource. The material suggests that 198 defences relied on evidence of aberrant mental state between 1843 and 1876. For Eigen, this confirms an earlier trend whereby insanity cases were constructed around offences against the person rather than property crime. Significantly, these cases reveal the first emergence of 'mental absence'.

It is here that the reader encounters problems with Eigen's analysis. Framing a highly detailed account of insanity trials in Victorian London with an Australian case from 1950, and emerging North American concern about multiple personality disorder in the late twentieth century, is original but problematic. While it makes for a very persuasive argument about the implications of the Victorian courts' willingness to consider 'unconscious crime', it makes it all the more necessary that readers should be supplied with more signposts to help them through what can be dense scripts, interspersed with complex arguments and subtle inferences. Chapter headings such as 'Do you Remember Cardiff?' give few clues to the important contributions Eigen is making to our understanding of insanity pleas.

This material is an incredibly rich source, but has its limitations. The medical testimony would also benefit from slightly more attention to its wider context and the professional and institutional interests at stake. Eigen makes an important point when he demonstrates that a wider range of medical opinion was being aired in court after 1843. While pre-McNaughtan witnesses tended to draw on experience gained in asylums and prisons, later cases included testimony from a range of competing specialists. Eigen examines the problem of disagreement between medical men and recounts an illuminating quotation from J. C. Bucknill, who suggested medical witnesses tended to be split between those who knew something of the prisoner and nothing of insanity and vice versa. This very point has led to important new work on infanticide and wider professional claims to expertise in managing puerperal insanity cases at home and in asylums, and it is disappointing that the reader is not directed to this literature. In a similar way, Eigen provides a nuanced account of contemporary concern over women's ailments but makes no reference to the expanding scholarship in this field.

My final reservation is that the cases selected for discussion tend to be lurid. It might also have been helpful to have given a fuller overview of the 198 cases than can be provided by the statistical summary in Appendix 1. This is an important book but it needs careful reading.

PAMELA DALE

Centre for the History of Medicine, University of Exeter
doi: 10.1093/sochis/hki012

Amy L. Fairchild, *Science at the Borders, Immigrant Medical Inspection and the Shaping of the Modern Industrial Labour Force*, Baltimore, MD: Johns Hopkins University Press, 2003. Pp. xiii + 385. £35.50 (hbk). ISBN 0 8018 7080.

This study explores the relationship between immigration policy in the United States and medical practices and discourse in the late nineteenth and early twentieth centuries. The primary focus of debate is the function of the medical examination of immigrants by the Public Health Service for communicable diseases. These included tuberculosis and trachoma, from 1891, and chronic conditions and physical deformities likely to render the sufferer economically dependent, from 1903. Driving this discussion forward is the surprisingly small number of medical certificates indicating defect, disability, or disease that were issued between 1891 and 1930, with only 700,000 of the estimated twenty-five million immigrants who were inspected at the nation's ports and borders being certified and no more than 79,000 denied entry (p. 4).

Fairchild has produced an engaging quantitative and qualitative history of immigration, in which the relationship between science and power underpins the analysis, and facilitates an original interpretation of the data that is both persuasive and accessible. The text is arranged in two parts, with an epilogue. The first develops Fairchild's central argument that medical examination functioned not as a process of exclusion, but as 'a tool for defining and shaping the nation's labouring classes' (p. 16). Certification indicated that failure to conform to societal expectations of industrial citizenship carried severe consequences (p. 160). Medical examinations largely consisted of a visual inspection lasting roughly 40 seconds, initially unmediated by diagnostic technology, and grounded in the conviction that disease was always apparent as a result of bodily examination. Immigrants endured both their own public inspection and that of others, at the front of a single file queue: a 'line of flesh and bone' (p. 7), which wound its way through gated pens in a series of repetitive and monotonous movements. Fairchild draws analogies with the symbols and principles of Taylorism, with the 'line' demonstrating both the rules of discipline and efficiency for the working classes, and labour's lowly place within the industrial hierarchy.

In the second part, Fairchild applies her theory to explore marked regional variations in certification and patterns of exclusion. The alignment of disease with class and race, supported by diagnostic technology and manifest in the manipulation of the immigrant examination, enabled regional concerns regarding immigration and the industrial economy to be addressed. In addition, the procedure epitomized the exclusion of specific immigrant groups in a broad attempt to 'shape a national Anglo-American identity' (p. 189). This is followed by an epilogue that briefly explores immigrant inspection following enactment of restrictive legislation in 1924. This marked the end of open immigration, and signalled a shift in the Public Health Service's power and authority to discipline and define the industrial workforce.

Although Britain does not have a direct comparative history of immigrant medical inspection, Fairchild's research offers an interesting comparison for the study of British Port Sanitary Authorities, and contemporary immigration policies.

Catherine Mills

University of Exeter
doi: 10.1093/sochis/hki013

Lawrence O. Gostin, *The AIDS Pandemic*, London: University of North Carolina Press, 2004. Pp. xli + 445. £24.50 (pbk). ISBN 0 8078 2830 0.

Lawrence O. Gostin has been actively involved in national and international policy-making bodies since the beginning of the AIDS pandemic. This large collection of updated essays both surveys the legal and political history of HIV/AIDS in the United States, and advocates public health and legal policies based on respect for the human rights of those infected or at risk of infection. Gostin's passionate belief about the need to protect and promote human rights is clearly mirrored throughout the 17 chapters of this book.

Gostin offers a refreshing ethical analysis of decisions to exclude and identify HIV-infected health care workers, and provides a robust defence of the charge of medical colonialism, especially in relation to the controversial trials of low dose antiviral treatment used to reduce perinatal transmission of HIV in developing countries. He also touches on inherent ethical challenges, such as the way in which the world community is currently responding to the AIDS pandemic at a time of 'complacency, injustice, and unfulfilled expectations'. As a result, there are a large number of recipients of injustice, particularly within the United States, where there are massive numbers of under- or uninsured individuals. For students of law, the figures, tables, and bibliography provide a concise summary of the vast amount of litigation that surrounds the issue. Somewhat disappointingly, there is hardly any reference to non-American legal rulings, and while the penultimate chapter examines the global reach of HIV/AIDS, the book suffers from being unduly focused on the United States.

DEBORAH KIRKLIN

University College, London
doi: 10.1093/sochis/hki014

M. Harrison, *Disease and the Modern World: 1500 to the Present Day*, Cambridge: Polity Press, 2004. Pp. 270. £17.99 (pbk). ISBN 0 7456 2810 9.

In this accessible volume, Mark Harrison tackles the formidable task of charting the history of disease from around 1500 through to the present day in 191 pages. Harrison demonstrates that disease was central to the rise of modern nation-states and their administrative structures, and examines the ways in which disease and its treatment and prevention evolved over this period under the impact of the Renaissance, the Enlightenment and the advent of scientific medicine.

Written in an engaging and lively manner and concluding with a generous glossary, 50 pages of chapter notes, a select bibliography and index, the work will establish itself as an excellent introduction to what has proved a very fertile field of historical research. While the first half of his introduction maps out the study as particularly relevant to today's world of international trade and travel, the second half proves a useful summary of the history of medicine during the past half century. In particular, Harrison aptly summarizes a number of the most influential approaches to disease and epidemics as depicted in the works of scholars including Fleck, Delaporte, Douglas, Foucault, Latour, and Rosenberg.

The work's eight chapters are organized chronologically, beginning with humoral medicine in the Middle Ages and continuing through to biotechnology. The first chapter examines disease and medicine before 1500, concentrating on 'the world the plague made' (p. 21). The next two sections cover theoretical and practical aspects of the early modern period, including discussion of syphilis and plague, the two diseases that had the most profound effect upon Western medicine during these years, followed by a discussion of Europe after the decline of plague in the Enlightenment period. In the fourth chapter, the focus shifts to the world beyond Europe, which has been the subject of much of Harrison's own research. It deals with the epidemics that resulted from intensified contact between Europeans and indigenous peoples. This is followed by a chapter examining how exploration, slavery, and colonization contributed to the process of industrialization in Europe, and considers the implementation of medical treatments, such as vaccination and public health reforms, which helped to protect rising levels of wealth in an age of urbanization and global trade.

The West was less successful in exporting health technologies to its former colonies and developing nations in the first decades of the twentieth century. This is demonstrated in chapter seven, which is devoted to consideration of influenza, typhus, malaria, and venereal disease. Although this half century of warfare ended on a positive note with the development of sulphonamides and penicillin, high mortality rates continued to plague large parts of the world 'despite the remarkable medical advances of the last half-century' (p. 191).

By taking what amounts to a global approach to the history of disease, Harrison's book becomes less a history of progress than of missed opportunities. Although this leaves the reader with a relatively bleak picture of medicine in our own times, it also inspires a degree of optimism, not least by redirecting attention from the history of Western medicine to other parts of the world. This is a valuable source for all those interested in medical history.

Jonathan Reinarz

University of Birmingham
doi: 10.1093/sochis/hki015

Martha Stoddard Holmes, *Fictions of Afflictions: Physical Disability in Victorian Culture*, Ann Arbor: University of Michigan Press, 2004. Pp. xiv + 228. £31.00 (hbk). ISBN 0 4720 9841 1.

Literary and historical scholarship has all too often neglected the disabled, which makes *Fictions of Afflictions* a very welcome addition to an under-researched field. This book counters academic and contemporary resistance to thinking about the disabled by combining approaches and questions from disability studies and literary criticism and seeks to reposition physical disability within cultural studies and representations of the body. Holmes asserts the importance of pathos and melodrama in fashioning an identity for the disabled in Victorian society by drawing on a body of literary sources, including the works of Dickens, Collins, Bulwer Lytton, Craik, and Yonge, and the concerns voiced by Poor Law authorities and the Charity Organization Society.

While literary works written by non-disabled people became a major vehicle for the transfer of cultural values about disability, Holmes argues that all representations of disability were affect-laden and presented in a melodramatic way. This reflects the emphasis on portraying disability in Victorian society in emotional terms, rather than through concrete examples or material lives. Such a perspective dominated medical texts, as well as the writings of disabled people and the activities of charities that endeavoured to assist the disabled, perhaps in order to 'fulfil the wishes and allay the fears of non-disabled people' (p. 191). Paradoxically, Victorian literature portrayed the physically disabled both as childlike and deserving, but also dangerous. For Holmes, the role of disabled women as lovers, wives, and mothers remained problematic, and she reinforces an existing historical understanding of medical representations of women. The same dual representation of disability is present in representations of disabled boys, who were seen as deserving, and disabled men who were often associated with fakery and begging.

Despite its obvious strengths, this study has a strong bias towards blindness and deafness, while paying little attention to other forms of physical disability, despite the presence of 'crippled' characters in numerous works and the involvement of many Victorian charities in providing medical or financial support to the disabled.

Holmes also presents the lives of the physically disabled mediated through middle-class accounts. As a result, too much uncritical emphasis is placed on the reports of Mayhew and Halliday and their chronicles of the London poor. There is little sense of other voices. On the other hand, the book provides a lively and thought-provoking description of literary and historical accounts of the disabled in Victorian England.

KEIR WADDINGTON

Cardiff University
doi: 10.1093/sochis/hki016

Jeroen Jansz and Peter van Drunen (eds), *A Social History of Psychology*, Blackwell Publishing Ltd: Oxford, 2003. Pp. 280. £18.99 (pbk). ISBN 0 6312 1571 9.

The history of psychology is an odd subject. On the one hand, it is taught in many psychology departments around the world in isolation from other humanities subjects, yet still remains a significant research topic in the history of the human sciences, championed by major scholars such as Roger Smith, Fernando Vidal, and Sonu Shamdasani. In the history of psychology, however, these two interests very rarely overlap with the interests of practising psychologists. Jansz and van Drunen have attempted to change this state of affairs by producing a textbook which places psychology in its historical context.

This book is a welcome addition to the internalist historiography of psychology and provides a new way of studying the evolution of the discipline by emphasizing two main features: 'individualization' and 'social management'. The essays, which are clearly influenced by Michel Foucault and Nikolas Rose, explore these two themes in relation to a variety of core problems. These topics include child-rearing and education, madness and mental health, work and organization, culture and ethnicity, delinquency and law, and social orientations. Attention to these areas allows the authors to explore many of the main currents of psychological thought as a response to dominant interests, and in relation to social forces such as politics and economics, as well as to culture. These chapters also reflect on the place of the psychological subject in this development.

All the papers have been well edited and are suitable for students who do not respond well to retracing Wilhelm Wundt's experiments or do not want to learn about Little Albert. There is a consistency of style that is rarely present in multi-authored collections. But it is surprising that there are no separate chapters dealing with sexuality or gender. Both of these topics have been subject to much work in psychology as well as to a great deal of historical attention by non-psychologist historians. Moreover, psychoanalysis remains under-explored. This reticence to attend to the details of psychoanalysis may have something to do with psychologists wishing to distance themselves from the long-term dominance of the discipline by psychoanalysis, especially in the mind of the public. Another reason for this absence has to do with the choice of topics. Sexual psychology would have necessitated more attention to Freud and his followers, and would also have taken us up to areas of applied psychology, including sex therapy and HIV/AIDS counselling.

IVAN CROZIER

Science Studies Unit, University of Edinburgh
doi: 10.1093/sochis/hki017

Morrice McCrae, *The National Health Service in Scotland: Origins and Ideals, 1900–1950*, East Linton: Tuckwell Press, 2003. Pp. xvi + 288. £25.00 (pbk). ISBN 1 8623 2216 3.

Power over health care and policy was among the most significant to be devolved to the new Scottish Parliament in the late 1990s. In the past few years, there have been notable instances of policy divergence between Scotland and, especially, England, over issues such as foundation hospitals and public health strategies. This has arisen, in part, because of Scotland's uniquely problematic health record, but also because, even before devolution, the country retained a degree of autonomy in health matters, even under the National Health Service.

As Morrice McCrae points out in this important new study, when the NHS was created in the late 1940s, Scotland was subject to separate legislation for a number of complex and deep-rooted historical reasons. It can be argued that these long-standing historical differences have to do not only with policy and administration, but also with social and cultural attitudes. Scotland has had, so the argument goes, a more collectivist, public sector-oriented attitude to health care than England and this has been manifested by, for instance, the fact that Scottish doctors were much more enthusiastic about the introduction of the NHS than their English counterparts. The take-up of private sector medicine remains lower in Scotland than south of the border.

This is a detailed historical account of the formation and implementation of the NHS in Scotland which employs previously under- or non-utilized papers and documents that illuminate health policy in the first half of the twentieth century for both Scotland and the rest of the United Kingdom. McCrae highlights, for example, the importance of the Cathcart Committee, a body appointed in the early 1930s which brought forward important proposals for medical reorganization, and he argues that the lack of consensus over Bevan's proposals in England was not to be found in Scotland. This is not to say that McCrae has produced an unproblematic work, as he somewhat overstates the difference between Scotland and England. While there were variations between the two societies before 1948, there were also many similarities.

In addition, although the medical profession in Scotland certainly had their altruistic moments, they could be as politically devious as anywhere else. The book also suggests that Scotland was a more 'proletarian' and impoverished nation than England and rather unfairly criticizes Charles Webster's official history, a work which actually acknowledges differences in Scottish practice and in otherwise much-neglected Wales. Having said that, McCrae is generally correct in his belief that the Scottish health services, and their influence, have often been under-estimated by historians. This is therefore an important contribution to our understanding of modern Scottish and British health service history. It is a book that should be read by all historians of British health policy.

JOHN STEWART

Oxford Brookes University
doi: 10.1093/sochis/hki018

Marcia Meldrum (ed.), *Opioids and Pain Relief: A Historical Perspective*, Seattle: IASP Press, 2003. Pp. 222. $68.00 (hbk). ISBN 0 9310 9247 7.

This collection of essays is the product of a 1998 symposium sponsored by the University of California, Los Angeles, Liebeskind History of Pain Collection to discuss the changing use of opiates for the relief of pain. The book is based on papers presented by both scientists and historians on the changing practices and cultural narratives which animate debates about the use of opiate analgesics, especially for the relief of pain in terminal cancer patients.

Although a great deal has been written about opiates as addictive drugs, we have much less about their specific history as analgesics, which is the most distinctive aspect of this book. Meldrum has successfully integrated the essays by ensuring that they make explicit reference to one another. The first quarter of the book focuses on the history of opiate use and regulation from the Middle Ages until the 1920s. Washington O. Schalick III's study of the medieval use of opiates, especially in France, is particularly interesting as it shows that issues of economics and social control were central to the discussion of opiates 'long before addiction and abuse became a focus of social debate' (p. 18). Another fascinating essay is Martha Stoddard Holmes' analysis of the cultural narratives surrounding the use of opiates in Victorian Britain. Carolyn Jean Acker, a leading historian of the drug problem in the United States, offers an insightful discussion of the professional and social context surrounding drug regulation in the twentieth century, although readers who are familiar with her work will find little that is new in her essay.

Despite the strength of these historical essays, this volume really hits its stride as it moves into the 1930s, particularly in terms of the use of opiates in the management of cancer pain. This theme occupies the final three-quarters of the book, which is largely dominated by the voices of scientists. Particularly noteworthy is Huda Akil's vibrant account of her own work, beginning when she was a graduate student, on the discovery of endogenous opioid (the endorphins) in the 1970s. Other essays, for example Christina Faull and Alexander Nicholson's examination of the work of Cicely Saunders and Robert Twycross in the British hospice movement, focus on the use of opiates in the management of terminal cancer pain. Meldrum's account of the discovery of the opiates, which shows an attention to cultural context lacking in other contributions, is an equally engaging piece.

Nonetheless, the text fails to deal with the use of opiates in the broader context it promises. Although the scientific contributors show themselves to be apt and able presenters of closely-defined medical and chemical research, they do not appear to be particularly skilled at questions of broader cultural resonance. Meldrum has included two of her own essays, presumably to help balance the predominance of scientifically orientated papers. Still, this volume offers much that will be of value to practitioners, historians, and also to those who are simply interested in this too often neglected field.

Timothy Hickman

Lancaster University
doi: 10.1093/sochis/hki019

Karen Rader, *Making Mice: Standardizing Animals for American Biomedical Research, 1900–55*, Woodstock: Princeton University Press, 2004. Pp. xviii + 298. £29.95 (hbk). ISBN 0 6910 1636 4.

The creation, adoption, and manipulation of 'model organisms' in biomedical research has received increasing attention in recent years, as a result of growing interest in the material cultures of science. Rader's book is not, however, the first historical account of the genetically standardized mouse, but follows Ilana Lowy and Jean-Paul Gaudilliere's study of its role in twentieth-century genetics and cancer research. *Making Mice* draws on many similar resources and themes, but also offers a welcome departure from these accounts by focusing upon the life and work of the early twentieth-century geneticist, C. C. Little, a passionate advocate of the inbred mouse, President of the University of Michigan in the 1920s, and founder of the Jackson Memorial Laboratory.

Rader relates the fate of the standardized mice to developments in Little's scientific agenda, shifts in the patronage of science, and the commercialization of its infrastructure. In 1929, Little founded a specialist institution for cancer genetics, the Jackson Memorial Laboratory. He was simultaneously enhanced by his appointment as Director of the American Society for the Control of Cancer. The Depression forced Little to down-grade his laboratory and to start selling mice, first as a stopgap measure and later to secure a reliable income for the laboratory. Its role as a mouse-supply unit continued to expand in subsequent years, supported by new federal funding for cancer research, and the sponsoring of research programmes that made maximum use of its materials. Although inbred mice and experimental techniques surrounding their use became standard laboratory tools, and other commercial laboratories began to produce them in accordance with Jackson's protocols, Little repeatedly failed to attract research funds. The post-war backlash against eugenics, the waning of a genetic theory of cancer causation, and a new policy focus on cancer cures all served to remove Jackson's mice from the experimental genetic context that had led to their creation.

In the final, somewhat peripheral chapter, the frame shifts to the Oak Ridge Division of Biology, where former Jackson researcher, William Russell, carried out large-scale experiments on the effects of radiation damage. Following the Second World War, this field attracted considerable government investment, and Rader argues that Russell's decision to use inbred mice secured their place within the post-war biomedical research laboratory. By the 1960s, inbred mice were widely adopted by experimental biologists and had become a standard laboratory fixture. Rader argues that their rapid acceptance derived partly from a rising interest in genetic effects, and from scientists' commitment to a universal set of research values, 'namely standardisation, co-ordination, efficiency' (p. 266), and to the fact that mice successfully negotiated the tension between natural and artificial systems in biological experiment, and the boundaries between human and animal. This is an extremely well-researched book, although a little dry at times. It would have been a better study if Rader had examined the practices involved in the creation of the inbred mouse, the people involved, and to what extent they were bound up with shifting understandings of genetics, nutrition, animal husbandry, and epidemiology.

ABIGAIL WOODS

Centre for the History of Medicine, University of Manchester
doi: 10.1093/sochis/hki020

Lesley Richmond, Julie Stevenson, and Alison Turton (eds), *The Pharmaceutical Industry: A Guide to Historical Records*, Aldershot: Ashgate, 2003. Pp. ix + 561. £55 (hbk). ISBN 0 7546 3352 7.

Exploring the history of the modern pharmaceutical industry is not a task to be undertaken by the faint-hearted. The records are often difficult to locate, poorly catalogued, and sometimes manifestly and deliberately concealed by their owners. Even when archives are successfully located and accessed, pharmaceutical companies often carefully control the records that are available to historians, allowing extensive use of heritage records (including published material or records of advertising campaigns), for example, but strictly limiting the exploration of records which might provide insights into research and development strategies, the evolution of key products, or financial policies. If those hurdles are effectively surmounted, academic researchers can still be frustrated by a company's legal department, which will routinely demand the right to veto aspects of the final manuscript.

As a result, any publication which facilitates the task of recovering and utilizing the industry's records is to be welcomed. Supported by a grant from the Wellcome Trust and with the backing of the Business Archives Council, Richmond, Stevenson, and Turton have produced a well-manicured, easy to use, and comprehensive guide to the location, nature, and extent of the varied records of pharmaceutical companies which are either British or which have British manufacturing bases. Arranged alphabetically by company name, each entry includes a brief history of the company, a survey of surviving records and their location, and a short list of further readings. As such, the volume will provide an invaluable tool not only for business historians interested in analysing the emergence of the modern British industry in its national and global socio-economic context, but also for historians of medicine committed to tracing the development and dissemination of particular remedies for specific medical conditions.

The volume also boasts three introductory essays by experienced researchers, charting in turn the early years of the industry (by J. Burnby), the industry's modern development since 1851 (by T. A. B. Corley), and the scope and use of the archives (by Geoffrey Tweedale). These overviews are constructive in setting the scene for novices in the field. However, they are limited by their over-emphasis on the business aspects of industrial development and by their lack of attention to the broader, indeed global, social, and political tensions surrounding expansion of the industry. In these essays, for example, there is little discussion of the politics of pharmaceutical power (including exploitation of Third World health crises), or of the possible downsides of modern drug therapies. Instead, the essays present a rather positivist account of economic expansion and unfettered medical progress. Nothwithstanding this criticism, the editors, essayists, and publisher have produced a splendid guide to company records which will provide historians with an essential companion in their efforts to clarify the quagmire of our pharmaceutical past.

Mark Jackson

Centre for Medical History, University of Exeter
doi: 10.1093/sochis/hki021

Mary P. Sutphen and Bridie Andrews (eds), *Medicine and Colonial Identity*, London and New York: Routledge, 2003. Pp. 147. £55 (hbk). ISBN 0 4152 8880 0.

This volume, the product of a conference held in Oxford in 1996, focuses on the issue of how different colonial actors defined their identity. The construction of identities, as the editors acknowledge, is an academic growth industry. This collection claims to offer new insights through the prism of colonial medicine's cultural heterogeneity. The latter, it is claimed, can serve as an ideal means for exploring the ways in which individuals or groups can construct their own identities. Eschewing, as it does, the grand narratives or even the counter-narratives of colonial history, the volume accordingly focuses on the local and the specific to expose the contingency and hybridity of colonial identities.

The six essays explore the perceived self-identity of colonizers, the construction of a new nationalist identity from a mix of the modern and the traditional, the creation of a modern identity for women in the colonies and the traditional healer's response to the challenge presented by Western medicine. The focus is primarily on the British Empire; four of the essays are set in Australia, South Africa, and New Zealand, and a fifth in India. The sixth essay on the Dutch East Indies provides a refreshing non-British contrast.

Arguably, the most interesting are those which explore the creation of identity through the encounter between traditional and Western medicine. David Gordon charts the changing relationship between Xhosa healing and Western medicine through the work of John Patrick Fitzgerald in the mid-nineteenth-century Cape Colony. Gordon shows that, in this period when colonial control was weak, there was an exchange of medical ideas and identities which, as he puts it, contributed to a 'dynamic therapeutic pluralism'. Both Western doctor and Xhosa healer were changed by their meeting. Maneesha Lal similarly explores the encounter between traditional and Western medicine in the early twentieth century through the pages of the Hindi women's magazine *Stri Darpan*, and convincingly argues that while the identities of those who wrote for the magazine were influenced by Western medicine, its canons were by no means hegemonic. Indeed, there was a simultaneous and interrelated revitalization of Ayurveda and the resulting mix contributed to the creation of a 'modern' identity for the emerging Indian nation. Both these studies fully exemplify the complexity of the interaction between the traditional and the modern, and between the colonized and the colonizer, through which new identities were forged. This complexity is further illustrated by Hilary Marland in her comparison of midwifery programmes in the Netherlands and the Dutch East Indies. As she demonstrates, 'missionary work' was as active in relation to the poor, southern, and Catholic provinces of the Netherlands as it was in the East Indies. This highlighting of a 'colonialism' within Europe itself exposes the parallel developments between centre and periphery which are frequently overlooked.

The remaining three essays focus on Australasia in the twentieth century. Suzanne Parry looks at how aboriginal identity in northern Australia had its roots in medical impositions. The process by which milk became central to New Zealand's image is charted by Philippa Mein Smith. Finally, Roy MacLeod re-examines the methodological issues involved; in particular, the difficulties of constructing medical biographies at the periphery, which do justice to the differences of the colonial, specifically here in the Australian context.

As so often with such volumes, and in the absence of a more extended introduction and conclusion, the full range of relevant issues, which a more satisfying coverage of the subject demands, are not addressed. Consequently the parts are more interesting than the whole. Nevertheless, the volume does provide six valuable case studies on which a better understanding of colonial medicine, and indeed imperialism, can or will be constructed.

MARGARET JONES

Wellcome Unit for the History of Medicine, Oxford
doi: 10.1093/sochis/hki022

Holly Tucker, *Pregnant Fictions: Childbirth and the Fairy Tale in Early-Modern France*, Detroit, Michigan: Wayne State University Press, 2003. Pp. xv + 213. £24.50 (hbk). ISBN 0 8143 3042 8.

Pregnant Fictions focuses on the medical debate over the processes of reproduction in early modern France and their representation in fairy tales written by women, who used their medical knowledge to create narratives that subverted medical and scientific versions of the reproductive process. Tucker uses two dissimilar discourses to analyse the growing medical understanding of conception, pregnancy, and childbirth, and the changing role of women within society. Growing numbers of seventeenth-century elite versions of folk, or 'fairy' tales, as well as less well-known texts are used to make her points. In order to provide a context for these fictions, the author includes the scientific and lay versions of medical debates on the process of reproduction, such as the growth of the foetus and the process of childbirth.

The book is divided into eight main sections which include an introduction, six thematic chapters, and a conclusion. Tucker's first chapter on 'Uterine Legends' provides rival accounts, in both learned and popular journals, of the reasons and outcomes of several pregnancies which were said to have lasted for up to 30 years. This is followed by a discussion of 'Fairy Tales and the Facts of Life' and the way in which these transmitted medical information to women. Although Tucker's approach is based on the access of elite women to medical debates through their contacts with the scientific world, this is somewhat tenuously established. The third chapter describes how fairies assisted midwives delivering babies, including 'bad' fairies who could damage mothers and babies, while the fourth examines early modern attempts to influence the sex of the unborn child. The preponderance of daughters in fairy tales is examined in chapter five. This is followed by a discussion of the development of embryology in the seventeenth century and popular attempts to discredit 'bad' scientific theories, such as 'preformation', through textual subversion.

While Tucker exploits her sources with some skill, the book would have been improved by a more considered examination of the social origins of the tales and their authors' medical knowledge and the access to medical knowledge which would add both subtlety and depth to her analysis. For example, several historians have suggested that elite writers of tales first heard such stories at the knee of their nurse, a fascinating and potentially fruitful line of enquiry. Even so, the argument that female writers used a particular genre to understand and perhaps to challenge medical ideas and practices is well made and documented. The social context of ideas, and hence their expression in tales, is less convincingly handled, thus limiting the appeal of this otherwise fascinating book.

ANGIE SMITH

Oxford Brookes University
doi: 10.1093/sochis/hki023

Social History of Medicine Vol. 18 No. 1 © The Society for the Social History of Medicine 2005, all rights reserved.
doi:10.1093/sochis/hki024

Publications Received

Catherine Blackledge, *The Story of V: A Natural History of Female Sexuality*, New Brunswick, NJ: Orien Publishing, 2004. Pp. xi + 322. $24.95. ISBN 0–8135–3455–0.

Alfred Jay Bollet, *Plagues and Poxes. The Impact of Human History on Epidemic Disease*, New York: Demos, 2004. Pp. xii + 237. $29.95. ISBN 1–888799–79X.

Geoffrey Chamberlain, *Special Delivery: The Life of the Celebrated British Obstetrician*, London: Royal College of Obstetricians and Gynaecologists, 2004. Pp. xii + 154. £19.50. ISBN 1–900364–98–0.

Harriet Deacon, Howard Phillips, and Elizabeth van Heyningen (eds), *The Cape Doctor in the Nineteenth Century: A Social History*, Amsterdam: Clio Medica, 2004. Pp. 318. €75 (hbk), €35 (pbk). ISBN 90–420–1074–6 (hbk), 90–420–1064–9 (pbk).

Alice Domurat Dreger, *One of Us: Conjoined Twins and the Future of Normal*, Cambridge, MA and London: Harvard University Press, 2004. Pp.198. £14.95. ISBN 0–674–01294–1.

Carl Elliott and Todd Chambers (eds), *Prozac as a Way of Life*, Chapel Hill: University of North Carolina Press, 2004. Pp 221. £26.95 (hbk), £13.50 (pbk). ISBN 0–8078–2880–7 (hbk), 0–8078–5551–0 (pbk).

Martyn Evans, Pekka Louhiala, and Raimo Puustinen, *Philosophy for Medicine: Applications in a Clinical Context*, Oxford: Radcliffe Medical Press, 2004. Pp. x + 158. £21.95. ISBN 1–85775–943–5.

Christopher E. Forth, *The Dreyfus Affair and the Crisis of French Manhood*, Baltimore: The Johns Hopkins Press, 2004. Pp. xii + 300. £33.50. ISBN 0–8018–7433–5.

Jane Fraser and Richard Cave, *Presenting in Biomedicine: 500 Tips for Success*, Oxford: Radcliffe Science Press, 2004. Pp. viii + 151, £21.95. ISBN 1–85775–897–8.

Stephen Garton, *Histories of Sexuality: Antiquity to Sexual Revolution*, London: Equinox Publishing Ltd., 2004. Pp. xiv +311. £14.99 (pbk), £65.00 (hbk). ISBN 1–904768–24–5 (pbk), 1–904768–23–7 (hbk).

Norman Gevitz, *The Dos: Osteopathic Medicine in America*, 2nd edn, Baltimore: The Johns Hopkins University Press, 2004. Pp. xiv + 242. £18.00 (pbk), £32.00 (hbk). ISBN 0–8018–7834–9 (pbk), 0–8018–7833–0 (hbk).

Sander L. Gilman and Zhou Xun (eds), *Smoke: A Global History of Smoking*, London: Reaktion Books, 2004. Pp. 408. £29.00. ISBN 1086189–200–4.

David Greaves, *The Healing Tradition: Reviving the Soul of Western Medicine*, Oxford and San Francisco: Radcliffe Publishing, 2004. Pp. 168. £21.95. ISBN 1–8775–963-X.

Sydney A. Halpern, *Lesser Harms: The Morality of Risk in Medical Research*, Chicago: University of Chicago Press, 2004. Pp. xii + 233. $37.50/£26.50. ISBN 0–226–31451–0.

Mark Harrison, *Medicine and Victory: British Military Medicine in the Second World War*, Oxford: Oxford University Press, 2004. Pp. xiii + 320. £45.00. ISBN 0–19–9268592.

Gail Hawkes, *Sex and Pleasure in Western Culture*, Oxford: Polity Press, 2004. Pp. 224. £50.00/$59.95 (hbk), £15.99/$24.95 (pbk). ISBN 0–7456–1670–4 (hbk), 0–7456–1671–2 (pbk).

Christopher Hoolihan (ed.), *An Annotated Catalogue of the Edward C. Atwater Collection of American Popular Medicine and Health Reform*, Vol. II, Rochester, NY: University of Rochester Press, 2004. Pp. 674. $125.00/£90.00. ISBN 1580461158.

David S. Jones, *Rationalizing Epidemics: Meanings and Uses of American Indian Mortality since 1600*, Cambridge, MA and London: Harvard University Press, 2004. Pp. 308. £32.95. ISBN 0–674–01305–0.

Cesare Lombroso and Guglielmo Ferrero, *Criminal Woman, the Prostitute and the Normal Woman*, (trans) Nicole Hahn Rafter and Mary Gibson, Durham and London: Duke University Press, 2004. Pp. xiv + 304. £57.00 (hbk), £16.95 (pbk). ISBN 0–8223–3207–8 (hbk), 0–8223–3246–9 (pbk).

Gregg Mitman, Michelle Murphy, and Christopher Sellers (eds), *Landscapes of Exposure: Knowledge and Illness in Modern Environments*, Chicago: University of Chicago Press, 2004. Pp. 288. $55.00 (hbk), $33.00 (pbk). ISBN 0–226–53249–6 (hbk), 0–226–53251–8 (pbk).

Angela Montford, *Health, Sickness, Medicine and the Friars in the Thirteenth and Fourteenth Centuries*, Aldershot: Ashgate, 2004. Pp. 318. £57.50. ISBN 0–7546–3697–6.

Carol Thomas Neely, *Distracted Subjects: Madness and Gender in Shakespeare and Early Modern Culture*, Ithaca, NY: Cornell University Press, 2004. Pp. xiii + 244. $52.50/£30.50 (hbk), $21.95/£12.50 (pbk). ISBN 0–8014–4205–2 (hbk), 0–8014–8924–5 (pbk).

Margaret Pelling, *Medical Conflicts in Early Modern London: Patronage, Physicians and Irregular Practitioners*, Oxford: Oxford University Press, 2003. Pp. xvi + 440. £65.00. ISBN 0–19–925780–9.

Volker Roelcke and Giovanni Maio (eds), *Twentieth-Century Ethics of Human Subject Research: Historical Perspectives on Values, Practices, and Regulations*, Stuttgart: Franz Steiner Verlag, 2004. Pp. 381. €64. ISBN 3–515–08455-X.

Brian Salter, *The New Politics of Medicine*, Basingstoke: Palgrave Macmillan, 2004. Pp. xv + 236. £17.99. ISBN 0–33380112–1.

Shulamith Shahar, *Growing Old in the Middle Ages*, London and New York: Routledge, 2004. Pp. xiii + 243. £18.99. ISBN 0–415–33360–1.

M. R. Smallman-Raynor and A. D. Cliff, *War Epidemics: An Historical Geography of Infectious Diseases in Military Conflict and Civil Strife, 1850–2000*, Oxford: Oxford University Press, 2004. Pp. xxiv + 805. £100.00. ISBN 0–19–823364–7.

Werner Sohn and Bettina Wahrig (eds), *Zwischen Aufklärung, Policey und Verwalthung: Zur Genese des Medizinalwesens 1750–1850*, Wiesbaden: Harrassowitz Verlag, 2003. Pp. 212. €59. ISBN 3–447–04822–0.

Steven M. Stowe, *Doctoring the South: Southern Physicians and Everyday Medicine in the Mid-Nineteenth Century*, Chapel Hill: The University of North Carolina Press, 2004. Pp. 392. $45.00. ISBN 0–8078–2885–8.

Sheila Sweetinburgh, *The Role of the Hospital in Medieval England: Gift-giving and the Spiritual Economy*, Dublin: Four Courts Press, 2004. Pp. 286. €65.00/£55.00. ISBN 1–85182–794–3.

Corina Treitel, *A Science for the Soul: Occultism and the Genesis of the German Modern*, Baltimore and London: The Johns Hopkins University Press, 2004. Pp. x + 366. £33.50. ISBN 0–8018–7812–8.

Jeffrey R. Watt (ed.), *From Sin to Insanity: Suicide in Early Modern Europe*, Ithaca, NY: Cornell University Press, 2004. Pp. vi + 240. £22.95. ISBN 0–8014–4278–8.

Paul Julian Weindling, *Nazi Medicine and the Nuremberg Trials: From Medical War Crimes to Informed Consent*, Basingstoke: Palgrave Macmillan, 2004. Pp. xii + 481. £60.00. ISBN 1–403911–X.

James Willocks and Wallace Barr, *Ian Donald: A Memoir*, London: Royal College of Obstetricians and Gynaecologists Press, 2004. Pp. x + 154. £26.00. ISBN 1–904752–00–4.

Michael Worton and Nana Wilson-Tagoe (eds), *National Healths: Gender, Sexuality and Health in a Cross-Cultural Context*, London: UCL Press, 2004. Pp. xii + 232. £35.00. ISBN 1844720179.

John van Wyhe, *Phrenology and the Origins of Victorian Scientific Naturalism*, Aldershot: Ashgate, 2004. Pp. xvii + 282. £49.50. ISBN 0–7546–34086.

Instructions to Authors

These instructions are merely a preliminary guide to authors. A more detailed set of instructions MUST be consulted and should be obtained either from the Assistant Editor or on-line in two formats at http://www.sshm.org/publications/journal1.html The home page of the Society for the Social History of Medicine can be found at http://www.sshm.org

1. **Submission of typescripts**. Three copies of each typescript, plus IBM PC-standard 3.5″ disk, (Microsoft Word), should be sent to Ruth Biddiss, together with the originals and three photocopies of any statistical tables, maps, and diagrams and statement of word count. Authors proposing to use illustrative material are asked to consult with the editors before submitting it. Authors are requested not to submit typescripts that are under consideration for publication elsewhere. The editors hope within 12 weeks of receiving a manuscript to provide authors with a decision on whether it will be accepted for publication. Authors whose work is accepted will be expected to correct proofs of their own article, and will be asked to confirm the article's originality.

2. **Preparation of manuscript**. All papers must be computer-typed, double-spaced on A4 paper with ample margins and generally not more than 8,000 words (including footnotes) in length. Longer manuscripts will not normally be accepted for publication unless appropriate cuts are undertaken by the author. Each page of the typescript should be numbered. In articles and review articles, footnotes should be numbered consecutively and placed together in double-spaced typing on a separate page or pages at the end. In the published version they will be printed at the foot of each page. Quotation marks should be single and not double unless they indicate a quotation within a quotation. The title of the author's present position and an address sufficient for him/her to be contacted by readers should be provided on a separate sheet with telephone and fax numbers and an e-mail address. An abstract of the article containing a maximum of 200 words and no more than ten keywords should be supplied on a separate page. A computer disc of the final version is also required.

3. **References**. Book titles should be italicized and place of publication provided, e.g. A. G. Carmichael, *Plague and the Poor in Renaissance Florence* (Cambridge, 1986). An abbreviated form of title should be established on the second occasion of use, e.g. Carmichael, *Plague and Poor*, p. 25. If the reference is to an article in a periodical it should include (after the author's name and the title of the article) the volume, date in brackets and the start and end page numbers (and then the p. or pp. if specific page/s are cited) of the periodical, e.g. D. Thompson, 'The Decline of Social Welfare: Falling State Support for the Elderly since Early Victorian Times', *Ageing and Society*, 4 (1984), 451–82. Subsequent references to the article should use an abbreviated form, e.g. Thompson, 'Decline of Social Welfare', p. 463.

4. **Tables and Diagrams**. Tables, graphs, and diagrams should each be on a separate sheet, bearing the author's name and the title of the paper, and should be packed flat. Each should be numbered, and its approximate position in the text indicated by a marginal note. Tables should be comprehensible without reference to the text, and must be typed, without vertical lines.

5. **Copyright/Offprints**. The assignment of copyright form is now replaced with an exclusive licence. In addition to allowing authors to retain copyright for the material, a number of significant rights concerning the future re-use of their article are granted back to them. This is with the one proviso that any activity does not conflict directly with the business interests of the journal. For further details, please visit the following website: http://www3.oup.co.uk/jnls/permissions/ or e-mail: journals.permissions@oupjournals.org

The publisher will supply the corresponding author with free online access to their paper (which can then be circulated to co-authors) and 25 free offprints.